GIRVAN, AYRSHIRE: J CAMPBELL KERR

People's Friend A

Contents

p128

Complete Stories

p6

p85

ual 2002

p14

Animal Magic

p104

p136

J. Campbell Kerr Paintings

p71

Dear Reader,

WELCOME to the "Friend" Annual for 2002!

Including 26 complete new Stories by favourite "Friend" writers, we can promise you hours of great reading. There's nostalgia, humour, family Stories and good old-fashioned romances to relax with.

You'll also be able to discover a wonderful world of gardens in our special series of features. Animal poetry by Brenda G. Macrow is sure to entertain and J. Campbell Kerr's paintings will take you on a scenic tour of Britain.

With all these heartwarming Stories and colourful features, you're sure to enjoy the read of the year!

The Editor

The Glory Of The Garden *by Alex Muir*

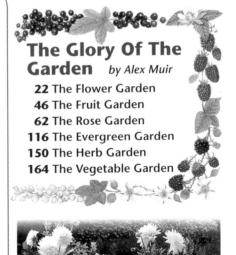

p22

That Summer In Aloch

by Margaret McKinlay

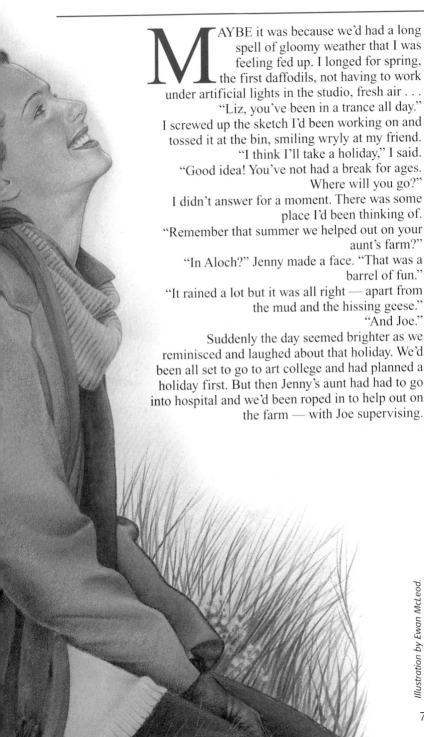

MAYBE it was because we'd had a long spell of gloomy weather that I was feeling fed up. I longed for spring, the first daffodils, not having to work under artificial lights in the studio, fresh air . . .

"Liz, you've been in a trance all day."

I screwed up the sketch I'd been working on and tossed it at the bin, smiling wryly at my friend.

"I think I'll take a holiday," I said.

"Good idea! You've not had a break for ages. Where will you go?"

I didn't answer for a moment. There was some place I'd been thinking of.

"Remember that summer we helped out on your aunt's farm?"

"In Aloch?" Jenny made a face. "That was a barrel of fun."

"It rained a lot but it was all right — apart from the mud and the hissing geese."

"And Joe."

Suddenly the day seemed brighter as we reminisced and laughed about that holiday. We'd been all set to go to art college and had planned a holiday first. But then Jenny's aunt had had to go into hospital and we'd been roped in to help out on the farm — with Joe supervising.

Illustration by Ewan McLeod.

Joe was nineteen then, the son of a neighbouring farmer. To be fair, we couldn't have managed the milking and other chores without him, but he thought we were pretty useless. Most of the time he glowered at us.

"Andrew was all right though," Jenny said grudgingly. "You should have kept in touch with him."

Andrew was Joe's brother, older than us all and studying to be a vet. We'd had fun together and had promised to write but, after a few letters, it sort of fizzled out.

"He'll be in practice now, probably in Aloch," Jenny said with a sideways look at me.

"If I go, it won't be to meet up with Andrew again," I said firmly, meaning it. I wasn't sure why, but over the years that holiday had kept coming into my mind. It had been a special time.

"February in Aloch — it'll probably snow. Things never look as good second time around, and Auntie Joan sold the farm, so you can't go there. Go abroad for some sun, Liz."

But Aloch was drawing me. I had a vague hope that I could recapture the carefree happiness of that summer . . .

I FELT a bit foolish the following week as I set out on the three-hour train journey. What did I expect to find? The impulse to go had weakened as the week wore on, especially since the weather had worsened.

Three days of sleet and snow showers had forced me to dig out clothes that had been at the back of the wardrobe for a long time. And it had occurred to me, as the day of my departure got closer, that the tourist attractions would be closed and I didn't know a friendly face in Aloch — unless Andrew was about.

I had booked into a small hotel in the village and found it much altered since I last saw it. It had been tastefully modernised and I was given a lovely room.

I didn't bother to unpack on arrival except for my sketch pad and went out to the harbour where the fishing boats were rocking in the heavy swell.

Men in oilskins were cleaning the decks and noisy gulls were wheeling round in search of fish scraps. The smell of fish was strong as I stepped over coiled ropes and fishing gear. Already, memories were stirring of the day Jenny and I had persuaded one of the skippers to take us out to sea.

I'd loved it, but Jenny had been sick most of the time.

I found a perch and did some quick sketches of the boats but my fingers were soon too cold to hold the pencil, so I retreated to my centrally heated room at the hotel. I went to bed early that night, beginning to wish I'd listened to Jenny and gone abroad.

Next morning, there was an improvement in the weather and, although it was still cold, the wintry sun was doing its best to warm things up.

I strolled along the main street and then let my feet lead me up the road that led to the farm. That summer we'd had bikes to explore the lanes when we weren't busy with farm chores.

It took longer than I'd expected to make the journey on foot, though the lanes were now proper roads. Other things had changed, too. New houses had been added on to the edge of the village and even the shape of the fields had altered with the disappearance of hedgerows.

I trudged on all the same until I saw the familiar farm buildings, which had been painted since I last saw them. There were the usual cattle footprints in the mud but the place seemed to be more prosperous now, a busy farm instead of the smallholding it had once been.

I WAS leaning against a wall with my sketch pad out when a tractor approached. Instead of going through the gate as I expected, it came to a sudden stop.

The driver looked down at me. It was Joe.

"Liz?" He jumped down on to the road and then stood over me with his hands on his hips — just as he had when mocking Jenny and me that summer.

"What are you doing here? Is Andrew expecting you?"

"I'm on holiday," I said lamely. "And I haven't heard from Andrew in years."

His dark brows came together in a familiar frown.

"We don't get many visitors in winter. Do you want a coffee?" He nodded towards the farm. When he saw my puzzled look, he explained.

"We took it over when Mrs Watson sold up. It made sense to join the two farms." I saw him taking in my clothes and my sensible boots.

"At least you're dressed for the part this time."

"We were on holiday," I protested as he hoisted me up on the tractor for the ride up to the farm.

He started the engine and had to shout.

"Andrew's got a good practice going now."

So, Andrew had qualified.

"How long are you staying?"

"A week, maybe, depending on the weather."

I was glad to see there were no geese on the loose as he helped me climb down a little later.

We left our boots in the porch and then went into the kitchen where there was now an Aga sending out blessed warmth.

Joe quickly cleared away dishes from the table.

White Horses

MAGICAL creatures of moorland and vale,
Featured in legend and chivalrous tale,
Carved in the chalk hills before we were born,
Weaving old spells like the pale unicorn.

Lovely in landscapes of colourful hue,
Visions of white beneath summits of blue;
Grazing at peace on the green mountainside,
Glimpsed in the waves of the incoming tide.

Creatures of myth, like the kelpie of old,
Tempting the wary, enticing the bold;
Then, like the wind, with a toss of the mane,
Racing away through the mist and the rain!

When days are dreary, and summer seems dead,
Leafless the trees, and the swallows all fled,
Nature may still hold a gem in her hoard;
See a white horse, and all dreams are restored.

— *Brenda G. Macrow.*

Pony above Ullswater, Cumbria.

"My mother usually pops over to clear up. I'm not much good in the house." He looked embarrassed, which surprised me. My memory of Joe was of super efficiency — but that had been outside, in the fields or the barns. He made coffee and we sat at the scrubbed table, feeling awkward now we were face to face.

"I don't usually bother about a morning break," he explained. "But Andrew's calling in to look at one of the beasts. You'll be able to talk over old times."

"I didn't come all this way to meet your brother again," I said quietly.

"Didn't you?"

I shrugged.

"I got a dose of townitis. I suppose I wanted to breathe fresh country air again."

He snorted, as if he didn't quite believe me.

T. Parker.

"You'll get that all right."

There was the sound of a car outside and Joe got up to look out of the window.

"There he is now. You want to come along? The beast's in the barn." He didn't wait for me to answer but went outside, leaving the door wide open. As I put on my boots to follow him, I thought he might be five years older but he wasn't any sweeter. Then I went out to renew my acquaintance with his brother.

At one time, they had been very alike in appearance, but while Joe had become broad and weather-beaten, Andrew had hardly changed at all. He grinned as soon as he saw me.

"Liz." He hugged me, then stood back and looked me over. I wished I was wearing something smarter than layers of jumpers and jeans.

"Still gorgeous," he said.

He had the power — or charm — to make a girl feel she really *was* gorgeous.

Joe was watching us from the door of the barn.

"I haven't got all day," he called impatiently.

"He's a workhorse." Andrew shrugged.

The cow made a fuss when she was separated from her calf so Andrew could examine it and Joe stood back, looking concerned.

"Want a lift back?" Andrew said eventually and I nodded.

As we left, I saw Joe climbing back into the tractor without a glance in our direction. We hadn't even finished our coffee.

"You arrived at just the right time," Andrew said with a grin. "You can be my partner at the dance tonight and my mother won't be able to push all the eligible females at me."

"Trying to marry you off, is she?"

"All the time, but Joe gets the same treatment. What about you, Liz? No-one special in your life yet?"

"I have a hard time fighting them off," I said lightly. "I didn't bring anything to wear to a dance," I added.

"It's a barn dance. Jeans and a shirt will be fine. I'll pick you up around eight."

THE dance was in a draughty barn which had been lined with bales of straw. When Andrew and I arrived, the band was already playing to a good crowd.

I was soon caught up in the noisy atmosphere, breathless from being whirled around by Andrew and other partners. It wasn't until we paused for supper that I realised Joe hadn't come.

"He phoned to say some of the sheep have started to drop their lambs. A bit early at that. I'll call by later."

I was introduced to Andrew's mother as we ate supper from paper plates and I stayed with her as Andrew danced with a pretty girl.

"That's Annie McNeill," his mother said, with obvious approval. "Everyone knows they'll get married, but I wish my daft son would get on with it."

I knew she was making sure I didn't get ideas about her son but she needn't have worried. I liked Andrew, but that was as far as it went. He was a charming man but obviously not ready to commit himself to one woman. Andrew's mother might have a long wait while he played the field.

The last waltz was at midnight and I wondered if it would be Annie or me who would get a lift home, but Andrew came looking for me. I had really enjoyed myself and told him so.

"Would you mind if we stopped off at Joe's? It won't take long."

"Of course not. I'm too wound up to sleep," I replied.

It had started to snow when we found his brother, sleeves rolled up, inside one of the pens with sheep milling about him.

"Five so far," he said. "I've got one in the barn for you to look at." He ignored me completely and led Andrew inside, where lamps were lit.

As the two of them worked on the sheep, I felt helpless. I went into the house and filled a flask with coffee and put on one of Joe's jackets I found hanging behind the door.

By the time I got back to the barn, there was another lamb and after that another. In the small hours of the morning, I found myself in the kitchen, feeding a tiny lamb in the warmth from the Aga.

I fell asleep and woke to find the lamb still on my lap under Joe's jacket. It was getting light outside and I got stiffly to my feet. Andrew's car had gone and I found Joe in the barn, looking pleased with himself. For once, the frown had gone and he was smiling at his increased flock.

"We didn't lose any lambs but there's more to come, mind. Now I'm starving." He took the lamb from me and put it in the bottom of the Aga to keep warm. I found the fridge well stocked and soon we were eating grilled bacon, eggs, black pudding and tomatoes.

"Your hair is standing on end," I said, leaning my elbows on the table. He looked weary and content at the same time.

"So's yours," he said with a grin.

There was no awkwardness now, probably because we were both so tired.

"Do you want me to stay and help, Joe? I know I'm not much good at this, but if you tell me what to do . . . It's a daft time to take a holiday so I may as well be useful."

"Would you, Liz?"

It was cosy in the kitchen and Joe was looking at me with a sort of shy need that he was obviously finding difficult to put into words. And there was something else in his eyes which made my heart suddenly sing.

"I'd love to," I said quietly. And, suddenly, I remembered that summer — the smell of the milking shed, the warm eggs, the sun hot on my legs. It had been hard work, but those weeks had stayed with me ever since.

"I love this place, Joe."

He leaned towards me across the scrubbed table.

"I always thought you and Andrew . . . He'll marry Annie, Liz," he said quietly.

"I know." Then I found myself giggling. "Maybe someone should tell him."

His expression changed slowly but it lit up his face. He was such an open man that I knew exactly what he was thinking. I always would. Not much charm, but who needs it when love is there for anyone to see? ❏

IT was so perfect," Hal said nostalgically. "One of those times when everything went right. Magic — a magic summer."

"Sounds great." Maggie didn't mean to sound grudging, but somehow it came out that way.

But her boyfriend didn't seem to notice.

"Imagine being seventeen again!" he went on. "Results through, a place at college — the whole summer before you, with nothing to worry about till September."

"Well, it'll be nice for you to be home for a holiday," Maggie said gently.

She loved Hal so much and knew how much he was looking forward to their spending time with his parents in Avonford. The whole family was getting together for Hal's parents' silver wedding celebration.

There'd be lots of old friends there, too, and Hal had been reminiscing about good times they'd had together in the past.

It'd be the first time he'd be home for ages — and a chance to introduce Maggie to his family.

"I wonder if Fiona will be around," Hal mused aloud now and Maggie looked at him sharply.

She'd heard all about Fiona Blake. She'd been Hal's childhood sweetheart.

"She's not married then?" Maggie queried casually.

"Mustn't be, or Mum would have told me." He shrugged and then smiled at Maggie's slightly anxious face.

The Right Girl For Him

by
Sylvia
Wynne

"It was all over between us when I went away to college. It seems a long time ago . . ." He put an arm around her.

"It's you I love, Maggie — you know that. And Mum and Dad will, too."

YET, Maggie couldn't help feeling nervous when she was introduced to Mr and Mrs Fenton later that week. But she needn't have worried — they were a friendly, open couple who did all they could to make her feel welcome.

Maggie and Hal enjoyed a few quiet days in Avonford before his sister and her husband arrived on the Friday before the silver wedding party.

There was to be a family dinner that night and everyone seemed determined to make Maggie feel at home.

Not for a moment did she feel left out as talk of old times flowed. They were interested in everything she had to say and she began to relax and enjoy herself.

After the meal, as everyone relaxed over coffee, the doorbell rang and Hal's father went to answer the door.

"Well, look who's here!" he soon announced cheerfully, ushering in an attractive young woman.

"Fiona!"

Hal greeted her happily, hugging her warmly.

Maggie's heart sank as she saw his gaze linger on Fiona once they'd drawn apart.

For the first time, Maggie suddenly felt out of place. She was a city girl, while Fiona had been born and bred in this village . . . She must almost be like one of this family already.

Fiona talked brightly about how lovely it was that Hal could make it for the celebrations, how wonderful tomorrow was going to be.

She greeted Maggie politely, but then turned back to Hal.

Maggie couldn't help wishing Fiona hadn't called round to break in on this family dinner.

Family . . . She pulled herself up. She wasn't family, either.

For a while, Maggie sat silently as Fiona talked about old times, feeling very excluded. Then she excused herself, saying she'd have an early night.

"Are you all right, Maggie?" Hal was on his feet in an instant, concerned.

"Yes, of course."

He kissed her gently goodnight outside her bedroom door and then returned downstairs.

Maggie could hear laughter from downstairs. It was obvious that Fiona wasn't leaving yet.

Maggie got ready for bed but couldn't sleep. She wandered to the window and looked down at the well-tended garden.

Then, suddenly, she caught her breath.

Two figures were walking close together on the moonlit lawn . . . It was Hal and Fiona!

Maggie watched, shocked, as they kissed. All her worst fears had been realised.

Maggie spent a restless night. In the morning, no-one seemed to notice how quiet she was as they were all busy with last-minute plans for the party.

Yet, once Mrs Fenton had gone to the hairdresser's and her husband to pick up some dry-cleaning, Hal pulled Maggie into his arms.

"What's wrong?" he asked gently. "You looked tired."

"I . . . well, I didn't sleep too well," she began tentatively.

"Me, neither! What a lot of rushing about there's been. I'm exhausted!"

Hal smiled down at her before pushing her into a chair.

"Stay there, I'll make some tea."

As Maggie sipped her drink, she couldn't meet his eye.

Hal burst out suddenly before Maggie could summon up the courage to confront him about last night.

"Everything's so different! It's not like I remembered at all. Everyone seems to be bogged down with problems — mortgages, kids, job uncertainty."

"That's life, darling," she comforted gently. "It's been — what? Quite a few years since that magic summer of yours."

"I know. I shouldn't have thought . . . I've been back since, of course, but not for long. Flying visits." He gave a great sigh and she went over to put her arms around him.

"You've changed, too, don't forget. Things do — and people. But your folks haven't changed, have they?"

He smiled up at her then.

"No, they haven't — thank goodness!"

"Any more tea in that pot?"

HAL'S parents looked so happy as they greeted their guests that evening. Watching them, Maggie was glad she hadn't forced a showdown with Hal, to spoil their big day.

Hal was standing beside his parents, doing all he could to make sure their party was a success. One of his uncles stood at Maggie's elbow, telling her stories about Hal.

Soon, Maggie's head was spinning as she was introduced to a procession of aunts, cousins, old friends and neighbours. And she wasn't short of partners when the dancing started.

Then, out of the corner of her eye, she saw them together. Hal was dancing with Fiona.

Maggie tried to concentrate on talking to her partner — one of Hal's younger cousins who was very interested in Maggie's accountancy job.

Yet it was hard to keep a smile on her face when she saw the way Fiona laughed up into Hal's face . . .

Hal came to claim the next dance.

"Darling, you look marvellous — everyone has been telling me how lucky I am!"

Maggie bit back a sarcastic retort. Then, sensing eyes on them, she moved into Hal's arms as the band struck up again.

"Maggie," he whispered next to her ear, "I have to tell you something."

"Well, don't," she snapped back. "Don't spoil the party."

He pulled away from her then and gazed down into her wide eyes for a few moments.

"Yes, I saw you." Maggie couldn't keep quiet any longer. "Last night — in the garden."

His face paled and he drew her to the side of the room and out through one of the open French windows into the empty garden.

"I wondered when you were going to come clean."

"Oh — darling!" Hal groaned. "It wasn't like that. No, I mean it — it was just a wave of nostalgia — coming home." He ran a hand through his hair distractedly.

"She kissed me," he went on. "I now realise that she thinks that we can take up where we left off!"

"Well, can't you?" Maggie said shakily.

He met her gaze wretchedly.

"Of course not! I don't want Fiona, I want *you!*" he said urgently. "I love you.

"I've been such an idiot," he muttered miserably.

"You certainly have!" Yet Maggie was smiling. He loved her!

"I want to marry you, Maggie — if you'll have me . . ."

"I'll think about it," she teased, as she went into his arms.

Hal was so happy, he couldn't resist announcing their engagement immediately at the party.

His mother hurried over to kiss Maggie while Hal's dad patted him on the shoulder.

"Mrs Fenton — aren't you . . . a bit sorry Hal's marrying a stranger?" Maggie burst out in a rush. "Not someone you've always known?"

"No, of course I'm not sorry!" the older woman replied, her eyes kind.

"Fiona's a sweet girl," she added, "but she's not the one for Hal. It's obvious he loves you, Maggie. You're the girl for my son — I knew that the moment I set eyes on you. And my husband agrees with me."

"Really?" Maggie breathed. The smile she got in return dispelled the last of her doubts.

Then, as Hal returned to spin her on to the dance floor, Maggie smiled happily.

His magic summer might be in the past, but they were going to have a wonderful future! ❏

I'M scared he'll ring and I'm scared he won't!" I grumble to my friend, Belinda.

She laughs, tossing back red hair as her fingers rattle over her keyboard.

All around us, the large open-plan office hums as everyone gets on with their job. A variety of heads — grey, mousy blond — bend over their work and the printer spews out page after page.

I glance at my watch for the hundredth time and back at the phone — it's unco-operatively silent. It seems to stare at me, and I stare back.

"Joan's watching," Belinda warns, glancing over to the supervisor's desk. "Don't you think you should at least *pretend* to do something?"

I feel myself flush. Of course I should. I certainly don't need an unpleasant pep talk about time-wasting, today of all days!

I scramble for my place in the column of figures I'm supposed to input and force my fingers to tap in digits which seem meaningless this morning. Then I glance back at the phone — it's grey and scuffed. And silent.

"Come on! Make Stephen ring!" I urge it.

by Sue Moorcroft

THE WAITING GAME

"Stop thinking about it and he will." Belinda seems to have touching faith in my husband. But I pull an anxious face.

"Maybe he hasn't given me a thought," I mutter. "Kay has to have first call on him. After all, she was his daughter long before I came on the scene. And, grown-up she may be, but she needs him, too. And her husband, Jack."

Belinda tips her head on one side and looks wise.

"Well, what do you expect, marrying an older man? But at least his daughter doesn't resent you. Some people in your situation have awful problems with jealousy and rivalry."

An image of Kay bursts into my mind — tall, kind and confident, like her father. I think of all the invitations, the family get-togethers when I've always been made welcome.

No, Kay didn't make any waves when I fell for her father.

Stephen and I had met at a friend's house and I was conscious all evening of his dark grey eyes fixed on me. When he'd crossed the room and asked if he could sit with me, he'd impressed me with his quiet presence, his dry humour. He made my heart skitter with his smile.

"Oh, no!" I reassure Belinda. "Kay's lovely! Stephen had been widowed for ages when we met. Kay wanted to see him happy. She's not the problem. It's Stephen! Lately he's been . . ."

But then, Belinda catches sight of my screen and interrupts me with a giggle.

"*Paula!* Brain on strike? Surely you know the difference between 'due' and 'overdue' by now?"

"Oh, no!" I dither over the figures and peep at Joan anxiously, ducking my head to avoid being seen.

Belinda shows me crossed fingers and makes a comical face. But I'm too tense to smile.

"Stephen, why haven't you rung?" I say with a groan.

I MAKE a conscious effort to get down to my work. Actitivy might make the day go quicker.

Five minutes later, I can't resist checking the phone for a dialling tone. The required burr is plain in my ear. I sigh, turn back to the "due" figures.

"*Over*due!" Belinda hisses. "Good grief, you'll get the sack at this rate!"

I try to make my stiff, clumsy, unco-operative fingers work. Everyone else produces the required rhythmic tap-tap-tap on the keys. But me? My fingers are just not co-ordinated today, as my thoughts spin around Stephen.

Oh, Stephen, I don't want anything to change between us!

Suddenly I *ache* to be with him. To share what he's going through . . .

I feel I could scale mountains, swim floods, leap chasms just to fling my arms around him, soak up his warmth and demand reassurance that everything's going to be OK.

But he's not been so keen on sharing his thoughts lately. No, nor his cuddles — especially in front of anyone else. He'll disengage himself gently.

"Act your age, Paula! Or at least act mine!" he says, trying to joke. I step back and smile, as if not minding *he* minds that I'm younger than him.

Then he smiles sheepishly, obviously realising he's made me feel awkward, running his fingers through his hair. His hair is still thick and floppy over his forehead, but it's greying rapidly.

He's bought some stuff to bring the colour back; it's hidden in his drawer. He hasn't used it. He's unsure about himself. He's reached that age when his body's older than his mind. And he doesn't like it.

I interrupt poor Belinda's work again with my sighs and frets.

"When we were first married, we were always together. But he's so restless at the moment, conjuring up an endless stream of activities that take him away from me."

Away from my lazy preferences for the cinema, or the telly.

"Where are you off to this time? Not football again?" I'll remark, watching him comb a sharp new haircut, ready to go out.

He just shrugs, without justifying himself, disarming me with his smile, a casual arm around my shoulders.

"I still enjoy watching it . . . now I'm too old to play." He used to be a stalwart of a local side, but now he pretends he doesn't mind being merely a supporter.

"And there's bound to be a drink afterwards?" I comment, trying to keep the nagging tone out of my voice.

He grins and drops an offhand kiss somewhere near me.

"Thirsty work!"

I'm still awake when he comes home.

"Surely I'm old enough to look after myself?" He groans as he climbs into bed.

BELINDA interrupts my thoughts with a whisper.

"Joan's looking at you again!"

I snap out of my reverie and make my fingers dance over the grey numerical keys. All in the wrong order. Thankfully, the supervisor contents herself with another warning glare, before turning to someone seeking advice with their work.

"You can't handle this, can you?" Belinda smiles sympathetically.

Of course I can handle *anything,* I think indignantly. Stephen and I can handle anything together. Despite the difference in our ages, we face life side by side. But my lip, traitorously, trembles.

Belinda's hand gives mine a quick, compassionate squeeze.

"Need a quick break? A cuppa? I'll cover for you."

"*What?* Leave my desk just when he might ring?" I shake my head

The Flower Garden

For A Simply Stunning Display

RAISING your own plants from seeds is always rewarding. Simply sow your favourite hardy annuals outdoors in a sunny site and, within two or three months, there should be a spectacular display of flowers.

April is usually the best month for sowing, once the soil has had a chance to warm up in the spring sunshine. Then the secret of excellent results lies in the preparation of a good seedbed.

Dig over the area where the seeds are to be planted, breaking it down with a fork. Then firm down the soil a couple of times.

After this, rake the area thoroughly, removing any large stones or debris which come to the surface. You should aim to finish up with a top layer of very fine soil about one inch deep. This tilth is essential for good germination.

Always have a plan in mind before you start. Try to ensure that short plants won't be hidden behind the taller ones and decide which colours will work well together.

I like to use a mix of old favourites such as clarkia, sweet pea, larkspur, cornflower, calendula, foxglove and nasturtium. With these I can create a lovely, informal cottage garden effect.

Take out shallow drills where the various seeds are to be sown. The distance between the rows depends on the eventual size of the plants. Short plants can be about six inches apart, but taller, bushy plants should have a spacing of 12 to 18 inches.

If the soil is quite dry, it's advisable to flood each furrow with water first and then allow it to drain away before you sow.

by Alex Muir

thinned out again to the spacing recommended on the seed packets.

Storing Seeds

THERE'S such a vast selection of seeds available nowadays, it's hard to know where to start.

However, before I make my selection, I check on some of the seeds I have left over from previous years. There's a good chance that some of them might still be usable.

It's easy to test the viability of seeds. Just try a small sample of each one, growing them indoors on damp paper, in the same way as you would grow mustard and cress. Make sure you identify each variety clearly. If germination is really patchy, it would probably be safer to buy new seeds.

When they are stored correctly, the life of most flower seeds is at least two to three years. It can vary considerably, however. I have had excellent results from seeds which were seven years old! Nowadays, many seeds are sold in sealed foil packets. If the packets remain unopened, they can stay fresh for years.

This soaking is usually sufficient to last the seeds through their period of germination. However, if the weather remains dry for a spell, it is advisable to water the rows from time to time.

After sowing the seeds at the required depth, carefully pull the loosened soil back into the furrows. Finish off by tamping down the soil lightly with the back of the rake.

As soon as the seedlings are large enough to handle, thin them out to about three inches apart. Later on they will have to be vehemently and wrest back control of my lips. "I'm fine! Fine! Really!" I lie.

She studies me. I gaze back through fevered eyes.

And the phone rings.

The sound's barely hit the air before I snatch up the receiver with an eager, "Hello?"

But it's only my mother. I grumble a bit about the Stephen situation.

"What did you expect when you married an older man? It's part of the whole deal." My mother's always down-to-earth! The age difference is only fourteen years but she makes it sound a hundred.

"I told you when you became serious about Stephen that it wouldn't be easy! There are problems in all relationships — and you're just going to have to get on with them!"

Capers Of Capricorn

YOUR antics fill us with surprise
  And, though you look so mild,
You mock us with your golden eyes
  Like some contentious child!

Your appetite few limits knows,
  On stolen treats you dine —
The garden hedge, the blooming rose
  The washing on the line!

You caper through the unmown grass
  Ignore the beaten track,
Run up to greet us as we pass —
  Or butt us in the back!

Capricious creature, friend of man
  From old nomadic days
What further mischief do you plan
  Behind that cryptic gaze?
          — *Brenda G. Macrow*

She's right, like mums usually are, but I don't feel like hearing it just now. With a quick goodbye I replace the receiver and glare at it.

Ring, Stephen, ring! How much longer? I know you've had plenty of your own worries in the last few months but, please, ring! My thoughts rage in my head.

He doesn't ring!

Personnel department rings to check if I can give holiday cover for another job. Someone rings to point out that I've left my car headlights on.

And, each time, I snatch up the phone . . .

The morning drags. Nothing goes right. My fingers remain like bunches of bananas, my mind hops about and settles nowhere, I feel like a nervous wreck.

Everyone else apparently breezes through their work, everyone else's phone rings but mine. My head aches. I'm jumpy and apprehensive. Ring Stephen, ring . . .

"Paula!"

My head, ache and all, jerks up at Belinda's urgent whisper.

"He's here!"

Who . . . Stephen? I don't believe it — it *is* him. He's never come to

the office before! But here he is, threading through the desks.

The other women all smile in sudden comprehension as they sit at their computers. And he's self-conscious, stooping, abashed at all the inquiring smiles and bated breaths. But he's also eyes-bright excited . . .

"It's over!" he says, as he reaches me. "I've just had Jack on the phone from hospital — they've got a little girl, seven pounds, Eva Marie! Kay and baby doing well!"

"Congratulations!" Belinda shrieks as she ruffles my hair and pecks my cheek. I'm snivelling, everyone can see I'm snivelling and I don't care.

"Come here, soppy!" My tall, older husband drags me off my chair and swings me round in the air and back on to my wobbly legs.

He laughs, breathlessly, brushing with his thumbs at my tears of wonder.

"Paula, I've got a granddaughter! I'm a *grandfather!* Can you love a grandad?"

"Of *course!*" What a ridiculous question! All I care about is that I'm in his arms. All the tensions and doubts over impending grandparenthood that have plagued him during his daughter's pregnancy seem to have dissolved.

His joy at a new life obliterates his worries about growing older. It's bliss to feel the welcome warmth, the familiar kisses, to have my old Stephen back.

"So!" He looks down at me mischievously, apologetically. "How does it feel to be a step-grandma — at the age of thirty-two?"

It sounds terrible. *Grandma!* But I tip back my head and laugh, because I love him. Because it's part of the deal, part of the whole package of me and Stephen.

I return his kiss.

"I suppose it's just what I have to expect . . . marrying an older man!" ❑

Days To Ren

Illustration by David Young.

ember Always

by Cathie Mitchell

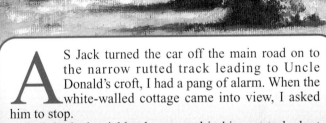

A S Jack turned the car off the main road on to the narrow rutted track leading to Uncle Donald's croft, I had a pang of alarm. When the white-walled cottage came into view, I asked him to stop.

Jack braked quickly, then turned in his seat to look at me anxiously.

"What is it, Dolinah?"

"Maybe this is going to upset him," I stammered. "Don't forget, he's an old man."

Jack seemed relieved, and he smiled and patted my hand.

"Dolinah, your uncle is as tough as an ox. And about as stubborn, too. Sure, he's an old man but, when I get to his age, I hope I can walk the miles he does."

"You can't look after a croft sitting in the house," I retorted, unimpressed with his assurance.

"Of course, even I know that. But how many men his age could manage a croft on their own? And keep a cow into the bargain?

"Though, for the life of me, I can't understand why he has that blessed animal. He doesn't even take milk in his tea!"

Uncle Donald was of the old school, for whom a cow seemed part and parcel of crofting life. But Jack didn't really understand that. He'd been born and bred in a city, where we had met and married and didn't always understand country ways.

Even now, after years of living and working in Portree, there were still some of Uncle Donald's habits Jack couldn't quite fathom.

Like his fire dousing act.

"Have to watch the chimney doesn't catch fire," Uncle Donald would explain, as he threw a pan of water on to the slightly glowing peats. This immediately created a thick volume of steam which sent Jack scrambling for the door and fresh air.

I did explain to Jack that my gran had suffered from the same fear. It was something that stemmed from their past. But, for one accustomed to central heating, this was a logic Jack could never fully grasp.

I did try to discourage Uncle Donald. Why couldn't he pour the water on slowly — try to avoid the steam cloud? He seemed to listen, until the next time he spotted a red glow hardly brighter than a candle. On would go a full pan of water.

Asking Uncle Donald to change his ways was like trying to move the Cuillin Hills themselves. Yet I loved him dearly and had done so since my childhood.

THE war years left a particularly strong impression on me as a young girl.

I remember Uncle Donald coming home on leave from the Navy — big, strong and ruggedly handsome in his sailor's uniform. What a great fuss he would make of me, bringing wonderful treats of sweets and other gifts from strange lands.

Toys were a rarity in those days, but I always had a doll, or a pretty dress. I still have the little koala bear he gave me one time on my bedroom dresser.

When the war ended and Uncle Donald came home in civilian clothes, I can remember asking my parents why he seemed different. He was quieter, less inclined to smile, or even talk to me.

Dad said the war changed a lot of people and Mum just insisted that I wasn't to ask him about it. If Uncle Donald wanted to talk about his war experiences, then he would. But he never did.

Was all that about to change now?

Of course, as Jack said, the war was a long time ago. And while Uncle Donald had kept his secrets, he'd also mellowed.

Indeed, there were times when I suspected that he took a kind of almost childish pleasure in annoying Jack. Many times I would catch a mischievous glint in those sharp blue eyes, hinting at the boy still lurking within that large frame. And he liked to put his foot down.

This was certainly the case with the two easy chairs he kept on either side of the open fire. The more Jack urged him to get rid of them, the more determined he seemed to keep them.

Jack would always complain about how hard they were.

"Nonsense." Donald would wave dismissively. "You need to get out more, Jack. Get away up into the hills. It's making you soft, working in an office all day."

"I walk regularly," Jack protested. "It's your chairs. Don't know how they can be called easy chairs!"

I usually had to turn away quickly to hide a smile. Jack was right about the chairs — and a lot of other things, too.

Uncle Donald's house certainly needed a woman's touch, so I visited at least once a week to tidy up, cook him a meal and help with the washing.

The washing can be a sore point. Uncle Donald persists in tying a length of string across his sitting-room and draping some of his old long johns over it to dry.

I always pull the washing off his indoor line and throw it all into the washing machine, reminding him we didn't give it to him as an ornament! Within the hour, I have his unmentionables flapping happily on the line outside.

The first time I did this he was rather taken aback.

"Do you think that's quite decent, Dolinah?" he asked, squinting out the window at the offending items. "My underwear hanging out there for everybody to see!"

"What everybody?" I challenged. "The nearest croft is the Campbells, and, with her four brothers, I'm sure old Morag Campbell has seen worse than your patched long johns."

Still, I told myself, it was probably a typical bachelor house; old socks everywhere, unwashed dishes, the smell of pipe smoke which I tried to clear by opening every window and door. But the nightmare was his sideboard, a large old-fashioned piece with numerous drawers, every one crammed with fish hooks, rusted nails, broken old pipes and some things I couldn't identify.

Uncle Donald said they might all come in useful one day.

"WHAT are you thinking about? You're very quiet."

Jack's question brought me back to the present.

"I'm not sure if he'll go to Inverness. He hasn't been off Skye since he came to our wedding. D'you remember?"

"How could I forget?" Jack exclaimed, getting on his high horse. "That's the only time I've ever seen him out of uniform."

"What do you mean?"

"Those old trousers and jacket he wears. I've never seen him in anything else! And those mud-caked wellingtons and cap. He surely wouldn't go dressed like that!"

"Don't be silly. He'll wear his suit, of course."

"Not his old demob suit?" Jack looked horrified.

"What else? It's the only one he has."

"But it must be three sizes too wee for him." Jack groaned. "When he had it on at our wedding, the trousers were straining at the button."

I couldn't help smiling at the memory and our daughter Jenny laughs each time we bring out the wedding pictures.

Jack hadn't thought much of Donald's suit, nor the black tie he felt was inappropriate for a wedding.

We did buy Uncle Donald a lovely bright tie for his Christmas a couple of years ago. I dread the day when Jack spots it tied around Donald's waist.

"If he does wear that suit, the car will be humming of mothballs for days!" Jack teased and I shook my head at him.

"No matter what he wears, it'll be a very important day for him. It's over fifty years since he's seen any of the people he served with in the Navy."

"Well, it's not actually someone he served with. Jenny did say it was one of the crew's grandsons . . ."

"Well, this man has come all the way from Australia, at any rate. So you'd think Uncle Donald would be keen to see him."

Jack shifted awkwardly in his seat.

"You know your uncle, Dolinah. He can be real stubborn when he likes. If he decides he doesn't want to go to Inverness, there's nothing you can do. Don't forget his blessed cow. You know how he won't leave that for too long."

"He'll be back the same day," I protested. "I'm sure he'll go."

A SHADOW fell across the car and I turned to see Uncle Donald standing by my window. In the long grass, his footsteps had been muffled.

"Are you coming in, or are you just here to admire the view?"

"We were . . . just discussing something," I stammered as I got out of the car.

"What you came to see me about, was it?" Donald guessed. The wily old fox! There was no hiding anything from him.

Once we were settled in those hard old chairs inside, I came straight to the point.

"Jenny phoned us last night with a special bit of news. She heard an appeal on the radio by someone who's trying to trace the crew of the

T. Parker.

Swans on Loch Earn, Perthshire.

destroyer you served on during the war. Anyway, your name was mentioned, so she got in touch with them and it turns out that this man has come over from Australia. Jenny gave us his name — what was it again, Jack?"

"Laird. Harry Laird. Seems he's the grandson of —"

"Tubby Laird!" Uncle Donald spoke in a kind of hushed tone.

Proud Beauty

ONCE the proud preserve of kings,
Regal birds with snowy wings,
Sailing with idyllic ease
Under overhanging trees.

Birds of "faery lands forlorn",
Ugly ducklings, laughed to scorn,
Till, in nature's magic plan,
Each became a royal swan.

Proud as any king or queen,
Now they light the sylvan scene,
Birds of ballerina grace
Mirrored in the water's face.
— *Brenda G. Macrow.*

I looked uncertainly at Jack.

"Jenny didn't say," I admitted.

"Whoever this chap is, he's come here to try to find you," Jack put in.

Uncle Donald was understandably surprised by this.

"All the way from Australia, just to find me?"

"Not exactly," I corrected Jack gently. "His company transferred him to London and he's taken this as a chance to trace you."

"Of course, he isn't expecting you to go away down to London to meet him." I added this hasty reassurance. "Jenny has offered to drive him up to Inverness. We're to meet them there on Friday."

"It's not far to go for us," said Jack, "when you remember this man has flown thousands of miles."

"But Dolinah said he was sent here by his firm." Uncle Donald put in the quiet reminder.

He didn't miss anything, I realised. He was still as sharp as a tack.

Those thick fingers stroked his rough chin in a now familiar gesture of deep thought.

"Friday, you say . . .?"

I spotted Jack's flash of impatience. I knew exactly what he was about to say. Some witty remark about Uncle Donald checking his diary, or could he not leave his precious cow even for just a few hours? But Uncle Donald spoke before I could.

"If I'm to go to Inverness, I suppose I will have to put on my best suit?"

Though he gave a grimace, Jack said nothing.

"Och, well, I suppose one day away from the croft won't kill me. What time will you pick me up on Friday?"

O N the Friday, Jack and I drove to Uncle Donald's croft in plenty of time. Yet he was ready and waiting.

"I've been standing waiting for nearly an hour," Uncle Donald complained as he squeezed into the back seat, bringing with him an almost overwhelming aroma of mothballs.

I craned my neck to smile at him, hoping to help him relax.

"You excited?" I asked. "Be only natural if you were a bit nervous."

A puzzled frown deepened the lines on his face.

"Nervous? Don't think so." Suddenly he grinned and brought a huge hand down on the back of Jack's shoulders, so hard I thought his false teeth would hit the dash-board. "I think your husband is more nervous than me!"

Thankfully, Jack hadn't started driving yet.

As we entered the hotel in Inverness later that day, Jenny came racing across the foyer to kiss each of us.

The man who'd been sitting with her got up and followed. I was surprised to see he was much younger than I'd expected — not much older than Jenny, in fact. But I liked what I saw. He was tall and tanned, with a smile almost as wide as his shoulders.

"So it was your grandfather who sailed with my uncle?" I said to Harry Laird, once everyone had been introduced.

"That's right." He nodded. "He emigrated to Australia after the war." He looked at Uncle Donald. "He talked a lot about this big fella, Donald McKay."

"You're his double," Donald put in softly, his voice a little unsteady. It was the first time I'd heard a hint of emotion in that brusque voice.

"Tubby — that's what we called him — was a nice man. A very good shipmate. And how is he?"

"Granpop died two years ago." Harry sighed heavily.

"Oh, I'm so sorry," I said. I longed to lay a comforting hand on Uncle Donald's sleeve, but I knew he'd be embarrassed. Emotion was something he liked to keep under tight control.

Harry looked round us all in turn.

"Your uncle must have told you about the time he saved my granpop's life?"

Jenny, less constrained than I was, threw her arms around Uncle Donald's shoulders.

"Not this big lump," she declared, her voice quavering slightly. "Never tells us anything about the war."

"Matter of fact, seems he saved two other crewmen when their ship was hit at Dunkirk . . . Quite a guy, your uncle."

This time I did lay a hand on Uncle Donald's arm. I wanted him to feel my pride and affection.

"I brought this." Harry Laird pulled a small box from his pocket and we all leaned forward to look.

"Donald gave this to my grandfather before he emigrated, as a kind of keepsake.

"Before Grandpop died, he made me promise that, if I ever got the chance to come to Britain, I'd try to find you, to give you this back. I was more than glad to. After all, if you hadn't saved my grandpop's life, I wouldn't be here now . . ."

Uncle Donald held the little box in one large hand and flicked open the lid. Inside, a gleaming bronze star-shaped medal lay on a soft white cloth. I couldn't make out the words as my eyes filled with tears.

So Donald had been a hero . . .

For a very long time, Uncle Donald sat with his head bowed, gazing at the medal. A single tear fell on to the medal and he brushed it away gently.

I squeezed his arm.

He wouldn't like me to say it right out, but I had to let him know how much I loved him. I wanted to let him know that he was still my hero — and always had been. He didn't need a medal to prove it. ❏

by Lisa Granville

Illustration by Gerard Fay.

Recipe For

Love

T
HE trouble with this agreement of ours, Jessica thought, laying the table for one, is that it's proving a pretty lonely business.

The way Mark had explained it, a trial separation had seemed sensible at the time. They'd been seeing each other for two years — wasn't it time they had a break? So he'd suggested three months apart.

Looking back, it probably hadn't been a good idea to uproot herself so dramatically. When the job offer came, it had been at the other end of the country. Hurt and bewildered by Mark's attitude, she'd accepted without thinking things through properly.

Now she was missing home badly. She'd left behind her family and friends, as well as Mark, and she couldn't help feeling lonely.

No good moping, though, she told herself. She should get out and meet people. Perhaps she should join something . . . take on something new. An evening class seemed a good place to start.

Supper was a quick affair and not very satisfactory, if the truth were told. How did ready-prepared meals all manage to taste the same?

Afterwards, she walked down to the local community centre to examine the notice board.

There was plenty of choice — everything from yoga to weight-lifting, feng shui to flower arranging. Languages, too. Now there was a good idea. Better French or Spanish might boost her career prospects.

Unfortunately, it wasn't that easy. There were two people in reception: a large man struggling with paperwork and an older lady who came forward with a smile.

35

"Can I help?"

"I'd like to enrol for intermediate French. Spanish, too, if they're at different times."

The receptionist shook her head.

"I'm sorry. Both classes are already full. Languages are always popular. Holidays abroad, you see. I could put you on a waiting list. Sometimes we run a second group, if there's enough demand."

Jessie hesitated and then took a deep breath.

"Really, I'd like to start something straight away. I've just moved here, and it's a bit . . ." Her voice tailed away.

The receptionist nodded her understanding.

"New places can be lonely. Let's see." She flicked through a file. "Not much left, I'm afraid. Unless you fancy car maintenance? Or plumbing?

"No? I thought not. Wait a minute." She turned to her companion. "Alan, could you squeeze in another one?"

Alan ambled over and gazed down at Jessie. Their eyes met and Jessie caught her breath. Somehow he seemed oddly familiar, though she knew, without a shadow of doubt, they'd never met before.

"Probably," he said, without taking his eyes off her. "Especially as it's such a little one!"

Then he smiled. It was such a nice smile, so heartwarming, that Jessie's awkwardness vanished. She felt herself responding to it. And to the twinkle in his eyes.

"I'll have you know I'm five foot three!" she protested, suddenly glad she'd come.

This man obviously enjoyed life and was probably great fun to be with. It was just a pity he was so . . . so what her mother politely called "well-covered". He was a complete contrast to slim and athletic Mark.

"All right then, Gail," he told the receptionist. "Consider my arm twisted."

"That's nice of you." Jessie smiled. "But what d'you teach?"

"Alan's a chef," Gail said, with some pride. "He's worked in London and Paris. And he's been on TV . . ."

Alan held up one large hand to stop the flow of praise.

"It's French Cookery for Beginners. Tuesday and Friday evenings. At seven o'clock — sharp." He was still looking at her, with the deepest blue eyes she'd ever seen.

"They're a nice crowd. You've only missed one class. You'll soon catch up."

"Oh," Jessie said, her face falling. Cooking. She might have guessed. "But I can't cook."

"No point in coming if you could." Alan laughed.

"No, you don't understand. I *really* can't. I'm hopeless. It always goes wrong. I ruin everything. I never cook. *Ever.*"

Alan raised an eyebrow.

"Sometimes," he said quietly, "it's the things we fight against doing most strongly that we need to take on and master."

Jessie had to admit there was a grain of truth in that. Learning to cook would certainly change her life. No more relying on beans on toast, or making do with a sandwich. No more last-minute dashes to the take-away.

And it would surprise Mark as nothing else could. Perhaps it *was* a good idea. Maybe it would make a difference . . .

She took a deep breath.

"OK. But don't say I didn't warn you."

"I don't scare easily." Alan laughed. "Besides, you can't be more of a menace than fourteen-year-olds who'd rather be doing martial arts."

He was quickly scribbling a list.

"Bring these items on Friday. I'll look forward to seeing you."

"Thanks," she heard herself saying, the thought of how impressed Mark would be over-riding any last doubts. "I'll see you both on Friday then."

N EVERTHELESS, when the time came, Jessie arrived with her teeth gritted, armed with ingredients and an apron, feeling as if she was going into battle. Never mind second thoughts, she was well into third or fourth ones.

"I'm terrified," she confided in Gail. "It's so much easier just to open a tin."

"What's the worst that can happen? If it turns out badly, stick it in the dustbin and put it down to experience."

"I suppose so." Jessie giggled.

After all, it was only a way of passing time. Nine weeks exactly. Then she and Mark would be back together again. No need to look for ways of filling evenings then.

Alan gave her a really warm welcome and seemed genuinely pleased to see her. Right from the start, the class went really well.

It was a small group, and the mood was relaxed and happy. Jessie soon discovered two other girls who worked in the same office complex as her and they arranged to meet up for lunch the next day.

Alan was a good teacher. He stood close by as she worked, gently teasing her, it was true, but also radiating confidence.

Unfortunately, he was concentrating on something else when she misread *one tbl* of flour as *one lb,* and added the whole bag to her soup. Minutes later, Jessie was struggling to stir a solid lumpy mixture which had already caught on the bottom of the pan.

"Good grief!" he exclaimed, fanning away the smoke.

"Told you so!" she retorted, wrinkling her nose.

"I wouldn't like to think," he said carefully, "that you were enjoying your failure."

Jessie didn't answer. She avoided meeting his eye and felt a pang of regret as she watched the others serving up steaming, aromatic dishes.

"Come on," Alan said, as they packed away, "one burned pan isn't the end of the world. How about me buying you a glass of wine to cheer you up?"

Jessie shook her head. Every Friday her sister phoned and she might have news about Mark. She couldn't miss that.

"I'm all right, Alan. Thank you, though. Maybe some other time."

"OK." He sighed. "Some other time, then."

Over the next few sessions, Jessie did her very best to follow instructions carefully. Soon she began to enjoy herself and take a pride in her achievements.

It wasn't usually easy, but Alan was always at her side to demonstrate methods which were mysteries to her, however simple they appeared to everyone else.

The group began to call in at a local wine bar after each session. Somehow, Jessie always ended up sitting next to Alan, which was fine with her.

They were often there long after the others had gone. Jessie really enjoyed his company — not only was he interesting to talk to, but he could always make her smile.

Just before the end of the course, he teasingly asked her if she'd like to come to a festival of food and drink with him.

"More about cooking?" She laughed. "No thanks! Even if it is in London. Twice a week is enough for anyone."

"OK, I didn't realise it was such an ordeal. But didn't you say you wanted to see that new spy film? It's just been released in London. We could have dinner and see it afterwards."

"It's no good, Alan. I'm not going to be bribed into taking a more active interest in cooking."

"But . . ." His smile faded.

"No. Look, why don't you take Mrs James? She's mad keen, she's already signed on for your advanced course."

Alan sighed and looked at his hands.

St Paul's Cathedral, London

THE impressive dome of St Paul's is one of London's most distinctive landmarks. The present cathedral was designed by Sir Christopher Wren and is an architectural masterpiece.

Step inside to marvel at the sheer scale of the dome. There are also wonderful carvings by Grinling Gibbons, and Sir James Thornhill frescoes to admire. A good viewpoint is the Whispering Gallery, where there's an unusual acoustic effect.

It's not hard to see why St Paul's is such a crowd-puller.

ST PAUL'S CATHEDRAL, LONDON: J CAMPBELL KERR

"All right, then. Forget the festival. Why not a day out in London? I'd even endure trailing round clothes shops with you . . ."

Jessie looked at him, alerted by something in his voice.

She hesitated, then decided she must have imagined it. No, as usual, he was pulling her leg. Of course he was.

"Oh, go on with you, Alan!"

And, almost in the same breath, he'd turned it into a joke. Just as he always did . . .

H E'S always so happy," Jessie said to Gail, on her way into the next session. "Big and jolly."

Gail gave her an odd look.

"What makes you think he's so happy?"

"Isn't he?" Jessie shrugged "I've never seen him when he wasn't smiling."

"Depends who's around," Gail said thoughtfully. "Maybe it's a defence mechanism. Alan's sensitive. I've seen him close to tears some days."

"Really? Not over our classes, surely?" Jessie was taken aback.

Gail didn't answer for a minute.

"And I wouldn't call him big exactly — he's more broad, I think. I suppose he does seem jolly — he has a real zest for life. Or should I say, he usually does."

There was a short silence and Jessie frowned, feeling she was missing something.

"Last session this Friday," she said finally. "We're making boeuf bourguignon, with a lemon tart to follow."

"It's got to be perfect. I haven't seen my boyfriend for three months. I can't wait to surprise him with my cooking."

Jessie shopped with extra care for the ingredients. She even bought fresh flowers for the table, and selected wine to complement her cooking. She was looking forward to impressing Mark with a perfect dinner when they met on Friday.

On Thursday evening, she went to bed early and was asleep when the telephone rang. She sleepily fumbled her way into the hall.

"Jessie?"

"Mark!" She was surprised he'd called. "I'm so looking forward to tomorrow. I've —"

"Jess, I'm not going to be able to make it," he interrupted quickly.

"Oh." Jessie swallowed hard. "That's a shame. Perhaps next weekend?" There was a long silence.

"Thing is, Jess . . . your job . . . all this time apart . . . What sort of relationship is that?" She heard him take a deep breath. "There's no easy way of saying this. I've met someone else."

Mark continued to talk for another few minutes but Jessie hardly heard him.

When she went back to bed her thoughts were in turmoil.

What sort of relationship is that? How could he say such a thing? He was the one who'd suggested they should part for a while. And blaming it on her job! He'd encouraged her to take it.

He'd never said he was sorry, but perhaps he wasn't. Had he been telling her it was over three months ago . . .?

She felt a fool.

WORK was bad enough after a sleepless night and Jessie could hardly face going to her evening class. But everyone would wonder what had happened if she didn't turn up. Anyway, there would be no meeting in the wine bar. This special meal was to be proudly carried straight home to share. So, after class, she'd be able to slip away quietly.

Jessie found everyone in high spirits that evening — except Alan.

He seemed withdrawn and not himself at all. He was still encouraging and helpful, but that extra something was missing.

Tonight of all nights, Jessie wanted him to jolly her along, make her laugh, cheer her on through her successes, help to retrieve her mistakes.

Jessie tried to pretend she hadn't noticed. She decided to make this one meal absolutely perfect, in spite of everything. Working with infinite care, double checking everything, she finally put the casserole into the oven with a heartfelt sigh of relief.

"Well done, Jessica," Alan said, and passed on.

Jessie's heart sank as she watched his broad back retreat to the furthest end of the classroom. Suddenly, she realised how much she would miss these classes . . .

But why? It didn't make sense. She still didn't enjoy cooking, though she was managing better. And she'd keep in touch with the friends she'd made. It was just Alan she wouldn't see . . . would miss . . .

Now that was plainly ridiculous. It wasn't as if he was a wildly attractive man — like Mark. He *was* tall and dark, but was hardly the slim and athletic man of her dreams.

Jessie stole a sideways look at him. He was staring out of the window, miles away.

A young student approached him with a query and Jessie noticed how quick he was to help her sort out the difficulty. And how kindly he did it.

Jessie furiously grated lemon peel, then suddenly stopped short.

Why ever was she comparing Alan with Mark? They were as different as chalk and cheese. Of course Alan wasn't like Mark — especially in the way that really mattered.

Alan wouldn't behave as Mark had done. He *couldn't.* He hadn't a streak of unkindness in him.

He'd been a pillar of strength for her over the past weeks. She really ought to tell him how much it meant to her.

Somehow, it didn't matter that everything turned out well today and Jessie felt little satisfaction as she slowly packed away her dishes as the rest of the class departed.

"There," Alan said, with forced cheerfulness, "that's your ordeal over with. Back to baked beans and packet soups now, I daresay?"

"I wanted to say thank you," Jessie said shyly. "You've helped me so much. I'm sorry I was so crabby at times."

"Nonsense," he replied, a bit stiffly. "It's been a pleasure. You've done very well."

"I surprised myself," she admitted.

They were alone now and she looked up and wondered how she could ever have thought he wasn't attractive. His eyes were so blue . . . and that smile . . .

"I was thinking . . ." she heard herself saying ". . . I expect you get sick of food, but you wouldn't like to come back and share this with me, I suppose?" she finished in a rush.

His reaction was quite startling. His whole face lit up and he moved towards her.

"Jessie! I . . ."

What happened next she never knew. Perhaps she started to move towards him, or maybe she nudged her basket. At any rate, the dramatic crash that accompanied its falling told her all she needed to know about the fate of the contents.

"No, no!" she wailed. "I knew it. Something always goes wrong!"

Tears of frustration stung her eyes. She bent towards the ruined feast, but Alan caught her, enveloping her in a gentle bear hug. He wiped her cheeks with a corner of his big white chef's apron.

"It doesn't matter. Really. You can make it again."

"No way! I hate cooking. I always have. Always will."

His arms tightened. He said nothing.

In spite of everything, Jessie suddenly felt at peace. She leaned her head against his shoulder.

"I realised today that it's you who's made these weeks bearable," she admitted slowly. "Oh, Alan, how could you ever be interested in a girl who loathes cooking so much?"

She could feel him laughing against her hair.

"Very easily," he said. "D'you think I want competition? Perhaps I need someone to curb my obsessive interest in food."

"Really?" Jessie looked up at him and smiled through her tears.

"Really, truly." Alan was looking into her eyes as he said it.

What Jessie read there caused her to swell with happiness.

She looked down at the basket. Nothing had gone to plan in the last twenty-four hours — thank goodness!

"Alan, I hate to ask you this, but, just this once, shall we settle for a take-away?" ❑

In A Changing World...

by Sally Bray

Illustration by Bianchi.

CHARLOTTE gazed down at her thick new Aran sweater and sighed with satisfaction. It was warm and snug and cosy — and looked just perfect with her smart, red kilt.

"It's lovely, Nan," she said happily. "It's the nicest jumper you've ever made me."

Nan smiled.

"You said that about all the others," she reminded her seven-year-old granddaughter.

"Well, they're all nice," Charlotte pointed out. Then she remembered

43

something and frowned.

"Will you still knit me things," she asked anxiously, "when you move away?"

Nan laughed gently.

"Of course I will," she said lovingly. "I won't stop knitting just because I'm living somewhere else! If anything, I'll have more time. When Grandad retires, we won't be so busy. You'll probably have more jumpers than you know what to do with!"

She laughed again, and Charlotte tried to smile. But it was a sorry little effort. It didn't matter how many times they all told her that nothing would change, she knew it would. It was *bound* to. It *couldn't* be the same.

She'd always loved having Nan and Grandad living just round the corner. It meant she could see them every day.

She and Nan had had such fun together. They'd shared strawberries and cream in the summer, and fireside crumpets in winter. They'd watched "Neighbours", tennis and skating and they'd had trips to town and walks in the park to feed the ducks.

And, best of all, they'd talked. They'd talked and talked and talked . . .

Charlotte had been able to tell Nan things she sometimes couldn't even tell Mummy. Nan had always listened, and had never made her feel boring or silly, the way some grown-ups sometimes did.

And, when her baby brother, Jake, was born, only Nan had understood how Charlotte felt.

Nan had understood that the last thing Charlotte wanted was a baby brother. She'd have preferred a sister if she had to have anything. Nan had also understood why Charlotte thought he was ugly and boring, and felt miserable when everyone admired *him,* even though Charlotte was much prettier and cleverer.

Nan hadn't got cross with her, like Mummy and Daddy sometimes had. Nan had been kind — Nan had understood.

Nan had told her it was actually *better* to have a brother, because being the only girl made Charlotte more important. She'd even said babies weren't always pretty, but that people said they were because it pleased the babies' mums. And she'd promised it would all get better. Jake would start growing up, and it would all seem different.

And she'd been right.

Jake was two now and, while he didn't look much better, in Charlotte's opinion, he wasn't nearly so boring. He could run, talk and play now — like a proper brother. She even quite liked helping to look after him . . .

And, best of all, he got shouted at quite regularly because he was going through a really naughty phase. He was often told what a good girl his sister was. That was really lovely.

And she'd never forgotten that Nan had told her she'd been there first and that that made her very special, because you only ever had one first grandchild. No-one would ever say that to Jake. No-one would ever tell him he was special, but she was. She was Nan's special girl; she always had been . . . But how could she go on being Nan's girl, if Nan was miles and miles away . . .?

She hadn't believed it when they first told her. She'd thought Nan was just going on holiday or something. After all, she went every year, always to the same pretty town by the sea, and sent lovely postcards and brought back sticks of rock and special, funny presents.

But, no, Mummy had told her, not this time. This time, Nan was going there to live. Grandad was retiring and they'd always promised themselves they'd move to the place they loved best.

Mummy's eyes had shone as she said all this, as if it was really wonderful news.

"You want Nan to be happy, don't you?" Mummy had asked her.

Well, of course she did. But how could Nan be happy, living miles away from her special girl . . .?

OVER the weeks that followed, she kept hoping they'd got it all wrong, or that Nan and Grandad would change their minds. But, when Nan and Grandad's house had a *for sale* sign in the garden and strangers poking around, it didn't seem like Nan's house any more.

Charlotte couldn't scatter her books and toys as she used to because they had to keep it tidy. Even Nan and Grandad seemed different. They both spent ages poring over photographs of houses; and Nan always seemed too busy to play now, or chat . . .

And, finally, it happened. The house was sold, and they bought a new one in the seaside town.

"It's perfect," Mummy said, "just perfect."

"And we're all going down there, to help them get things straight," she went on happily. "We'll stay in a hotel while they move into their new house. It'll be just like a holiday."

Well, it wasn't like any holiday Charlotte had ever known.

Oh, it was the same in some ways; taking Tammy to the cattery and stopping the milk and the papers, and cases coming down from the loft to be filled with all the clothes they'd need. But before, going on holiday had always been fun; this time it was miserable.

For one thing, it wasn't really a holiday at all. And for another thing it was only happening because Nan was leaving.

So, when they finally set off, she felt none of the excitement that normally came with holidays. The weather didn't help either, because it was all grey and wet and gloomy. And Jake was a complete pest in the car, pulling her hair and throwing sweet wrappers at her from his baby seat.

Frustrated and furious, Charlotte threw one of the wrappers back.

"Mummy!" Jake wailed instantly.

"Charlotte!" Mummy snapped severely.

"But *he* started it!"

The Fruit Garden

Planning Ahead

IF you'd like to enjoy delicious soft fruit during the summer, you'll have to plan ahead. Soft fruit bushes should be planted at any point throughout their dormant season — that is, between leaf fall and bud burst.

All soft fruits need to grow in a rich soil which can retain lots of moisture throughout the summer. So, before planting, I dig over the site thoroughly, working in plenty of garden compost or well-rotted farmyard manure.

The bushes must be set into the soil at the correct depth. As a guide, look for the original soil mark on the stem, then set in the bush so it is sitting at the same level.

Blackcurrants, however, should be planted about one inch deeper than they were in the nursery.

Make sure each planting hole is wide enough to let the roots spread out naturally. As you fill in the hole, tread down the soil so there are no air pockets.

As the aim is to encourage the development of a strong root system and vigorous new shoots, the bushes will now have to be severely pruned back.

Raspberries and brambles should be cut back to about one foot from soil level.

On gooseberries and redcurrants, the leading shoots should be trimmed back to half of their original length.

With blackcurrant bushes, pruning is really harsh. They have

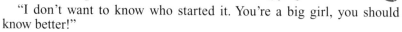

"I don't want to know who started it. You're a big girl, you should know better!"

And, on top of all that, she had to share a room with him.

"Why?" she protested. "He sings in his sleep and keeps me awake."

"Oh, Charlotte, be good. You can't have a room each because it's too expensive. And Daddy and I will be just through here, see, so you can get to us if you need us."

"Why isn't Nan staying with us?" Charlotte demanded. "She always stayed here before, you said so. Why isn't she staying here now?"

"Because she's staying in her new house," Mummy said.

"We can't stay there because they haven't got things straight yet."

Oh, it was an awful day. And, as far as Charlotte could see, things could only get worse.

Next morning, they drove the short distance to Nan's new house.

"Look, Charlotte, Nan can see the sea from her windows," Mummy said. "Won't that be nice for her?"

Charlotte said nothing. She couldn't imagine Nan living in this place, to be cut back to an outward-pointing bud about two inches above the soil.

The Sweetest Fruits

IF you're short of space, you can still grow your own fruit. Strawberries can be grown in all sorts of containers.

Try them in hanging baskets in a sunroom, or in pots on a sunny window-sill.

You can even extend the season right through from April to October by growing a selection of early, mid-season and late varieties. Growing the plants in a greenhouse can produce fruits as early as April and May.

Open garden crops will provide berries in June and July, and "perpetual" plants will continue the season until the autumn.

To plant up a barrel or tub, first make holes about one inch in diameter in the sides. Place them at varying levels and about eighteen inches apart. Make sure there are drainage holes in the base.

Place a layer of large broken crocks in first, then cover this with a layer of turf, grass side down. Fill the tub with a suitable compost mixture, which has been enriched with some well-decayed manure and a handful of bonemeal.

A little coarse sand mixed through the compost will help to improve the drainage. When the tub is filled, the top of the compost should be one inch below the rim.

Place the tub in a sheltered, but sunny, position and make sure that the compost is never allowed to dry out. Don't overwater, as this can also be harmful.

by Alex Muir

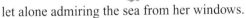

let alone admiring the sea from her windows.

They went inside, and there was much hugging and kissing and loud grown-up exclaiming about houses and furniture. It was nothing like any other time they'd visited Nan and Grandad.

Grandad had already started redecorating one room, and soon everyone was piling in there to pitch in and help. Charlotte trailed after them.

She watched for a while, but it wasn't much fun. No-one seemed to know or care whether she was there or not, and all the laugh and chatter was making her head hurt. They laughed even more when her dad hoisted Jake and let him tear off a great strip of paper, and Jake laughed, too, as if he'd done something clever.

Charlotte glowered. How could they be so stupid? He'd only start on the wallpaper at home, and then they'd probably blame her. And she wouldn't even have Nan to stick up for her, now.

She'd had enough. Cautiously, she took a step backwards; and then another, and another. No-one noticed; no-one even looked round.

Inch by inch she edged out to the hall, then wandered down to another room. There was furniture in this one, Nan's furniture, looking strange and out of place, as if it knew it didn't belong.

Charlotte made her way to the window. You could see right across the road from here, all the way to the beach and sea.

Tears stung. Why couldn't her mum and dad move down here? Then they could still be together, and she could still see Nan; and everything would be as it always had . . .

"There you are," said a much-loved voice, very gently. "I was wondering where you'd got to. What are you doing all on your own?"

Nan sounded just as she always had. Charlotte's throat tightened; she couldn't look round.

"Nothing," she muttered. "Just thinking."

"Ah, I see." Nan didn't say anything else. She always knew that some things were private, however little you were.

She moved closer, joining Charlotte at the window.

"It's nice, isn't it?" she said softly. "I shall be able to wake up every morning and look outside at the sea. And, do you know, that's something I've always wanted? Right from when I was your age, I always dreamed of living by the sea. When I was very young I always cried at the end of holidays.

"Remember you once said you wished Christmas could last for ever? Well, I was like that with holidays . . .

"Come on, sweetheart." She'd heard the sob that Charlotte couldn't hide. "Come and tell your old nan, now. Let's put it all right . . ."

AND Charlotte cried even more as she realised that Nan understood; that Nan had always understood. "You don't want us to go, do you? I know, baby, I know. And we never should have told you that nothing would change. Things do change, they change all the time, and when they do we need time to get used to them . . . It's a change for me, too. It's all new to me, as well . . ."

She rocked Charlotte gently, whispering lovingly.

"Do you know I kept waking up last night and wondering where I was, because I'm so used to our old house? I couldn't understand why the room seemed different. I need time to get used to this one, and all its funny different ways. And you need time to get used to things, too . . .

"Yes, it will be different. It will seem funny when we're not just down the road any more, and we can't just pop round any time. I'll miss all that, too.

"We had to think very hard about coming here. But the old house was too big for us, it had been for a long time. And we like it here, and we'd always promised ourselves we'd live here one day. But that's never going to mean we'd forget about you.

"I'll still be your nan," she promised very softly as she smiled and smoothed Charlotte's hair.

"And, you know, in some ways it won't be so very different. We won't be that far apart. You saw how quickly your daddy drove here, didn't you? So you'll be able to come and see us, any time you like — and we can come back to see you.

"You've got a spare bedroom, haven't you? So we can come and stay. We'll be your guests. Won't that be fun?

"And we can talk on the phone," she went on lovingly. "We can talk every weekend, every night if you like. In fact, I'd like us to. I shall want to know all the news. I shall want you to tell me everything, just like you always have. I could never, ever, do without our chats.

"Some things never change, love. The house might be different, but we're still part of each other, just like we always were. And, always remember, this is your home, too, just like our old one was.

"But you know," she went on, looking around, "it does need a bit of work.

"The people who lived here before have left all these carpets and curtains, but they aren't very nice, are they? So I'll have to go out soon and see about getting some new ones. And that's where I'm going to need your help, young lady."

"Me . . .?" Charlotte stared.

"Absolutely." Nan nodded. "You know your grandad gets bored stiff in shops."

Charlotte giggled, because it was true. Her grandad really hated shopping.

"There, then," Nan said lovingly. "You'll be much more help. Don't you remember choosing the material for your bedroom curtains at home?"

"When I helped you make them as well?"

"That's right."

"And I can help you choose the ones for here? And help you make them, too?"

"I wouldn't have any fun, would I, doing it without you?"

"When can we go?" Charlotte asked eagerly. It was beginning to sound exciting.

"As soon as you like." Nan laughed. "This afternoon, this morning; right now, if you want.

"We'll go and have a grand time in the shops, shall we? Just like we always have."

She hugged her, and Charlotte snuggled close.

"We'll do everything we've always done," she promised. "Everything we've always done."

And, at last, Charlotte knew she could believe it.

"I think red would look nice," she whispered. "Red curtains."

"Do you know, so do I? So we'll see what we can find, shall we?"

"See what we can find together, just the two of us. Just me, and my special girl . . ." ❏

Illustration by John Hancock.

by
Jane
O'Hare

TAMMY was counting another dandelion clock. This was the third, and it had to say yes.

"She will, she won't . . ." Now a great breath to blow off the last.

"She will! Mum *will* get married again!"

Sighing with relief, Tammy relaxed on the grass, gazing upwards. It was a lovely day — so bright that she was squinting.

Mum said she oughtn't to squint, but she couldn't help it when the light was bright. Mr Daniels, the optician, said she should have tinted lenses for bright weather.

But tinted lenses were dearer, and Mum had to scrimp as it was. She'd tell Tammy it was worth it to go on living in the house Dad had built for them . . .

The trouble was, Tammy no longer felt sure it *was* worth it, though she couldn't bring herself to say so.

She sat up, looking around the rather messy garden. They tried to keep it tidy in the time left over after school, work, housework and homework . . .

THE CONSPIRATORS

It would be good to have a nice garden where they could have barbecues, like the Wainwrights.

"Hi! Have some gum?"

Speak of angels! Gary Wainwright, aged fifteen like Tammy, stood at the back fence.

"Why so glum, chum? Have some gum!" he said again. When Tammy pulled a face, he heaved himself over the fence and came to drop down beside her, holding out her favourite sugarfree chewing gum.

She took it, chewed, and felt better.

"Thanks. I'm not glum. Just in retrospective mood . . ."

"What are you *retrospecting* about?" He smiled at her, lazily.

"Mum's boyfriends."

Gary sat up.

"Oh, Tammy! Not again!"

"Mum's possible boyfriends, then," Tammy added hastily, "whom she's shown no interest in! Or not enough."

"How many is it now?" Gary pulled at the long grass.

"Three." She marked them off on her fingers. "John Hughes, accountant. Paul Groves, dentist. James Arnold, newsagent."

Gary shook his head.

"You know, if your mum was to get *retrospective* about these guys who've tried to get into her life, she just might see a link between them and you. What do you think?"

"Mum never gets retrospective. If she did, she might come to her senses and see that getting married again is a good idea!"

"Oh, Tammy." Gary sighed. "I don't understand why you want to marry your mum off. I know you think it'll be easier for you to start your own life when the time comes. But that won't be for ages yet."

"Only two and a half years!" Tammy objected. "That's if I've got all the necessary passes for physiotherapy. They take you at seventeen and a half."

"That's yonks away." Gary lay back down. "Anything could happen in that time. She might meet someone you don't know about, and marry overnight!

"You know," he went on, "I'm not sure how I'd feel if Dad got married again . . . I don't think I could go through all that again."

"It might be different. He mightn't quarrel so much with someone new."

"Well, he was a bear with a permanent sore head before Mum and I left. He's great now he's on his own — just like he always used to be. You know how he is."

It was hard to picture Bob Wainwright being short tempered. He always had time for her, even if Gary wasn't visiting.

But then, she told herself, you had to live with someone to really know them. A pity you couldn't have a husband on a sale or return basis! She giggled at the idea.

"What's the joke?" Gary asked, then chuckled when she told him.

"So, how do you think it's going to go with your mum and this last one, the optician?"

"I shall know when she comes back from her appointment. Providing he's asked her out, like I all but told him to!

"He looked so sympathetic when I said Mum thought he was attractive, but was too shy to ask him out. The usual, you know?"

Gary cast an agonised glance skywards. He knew!

SARA was heading for home, Tammy, and a good sorting out when a car drew up beside her.

"You can't have a train to catch, you're pointed in the wrong direction!" Bob Wainwright said. "Want a lift? And what's up?"

"It's Tammy!" Sara settled beside him. "I was right, Bob. She *has* been trying to fix me up with another husband!

"Daniels, the optician, has just spent half an hour breathing heavily at me and asking me to have dinner with him.

"I asked outright what put the idea into his head and he said Tammy! So I'm going to have it out with her.

"And, Bob, I think we should tell the kids about us. Now."

"I agree, sweetheart. But I don't think you should tell Tammy while you're feeling so annoyed with her."

"And I don't want to upset Gary. If he's sweet on Tammy . . ."

"Are you sure he looks on her as a sweetheart, Bob? Not just a friend?"

"I tried to explore that over the weekend, but I got nowhere," Bob said.

"What I did get was a sneaking suspicion he's guessed about you and me. You should have seen him dodging. He was doing his best to keep from having it confirmed!"

"You mean he doesn't want me as his stepmother?"

Bob grimaced.

"Maybe. To be honest, he's always been against me marrying again. Nan and I argued quite a lot towards the end, you see, and I think it's scared him off the idea . . ."

He drew up outside the house.

"I hope you're wrong about Gary's feelings. Unfortunately, I'm right about Tammy being so attached to our place. I feel to blame for that — I clung to it, for us both."

"Which makes it harder to move on."

He took her hand.

"Leave the past behind and start again, together. Tammy's got to want to do that as well, or it'll never work."

She nodded, and they kissed gently.

Then they drew apart, because it was still daylight, and one or other of

Feathered Friends

ON old canals and waterways
   They often raise their fluffy brood;
Quite fearless, in those halcyon days
They cluster round the boats for food:

The drakes in striking plumage dressed,
With handsome heads of glossy green;
The speckled ducks with downy breast,
And ducklings to complete the scene.

Their noisy antics make us smile
When titbits overboard we drop —
They cross the road in single file,
And bring all traffic to a stop!

Yet spirits of the air they seem
When, in the dawn, they take to flight
And soar above the misty stream
Like arrows in the pearly light

Till, on the fringes of the land,
Where tireless tides slip slowly by,
They rest upon some lonely strand
And share the peace of sea and sky.
          — *Brenda G. Macrow.*

W. Shand.

the children might come along.

"I'm still going to tell Tammy exactly what I think about trying to fix me up with her optician. And ask how many times she's done it before!"

Sara could remember Jim Arnold in the corner shop admitting he wouldn't have dared approach her without encouragement from Tammy . . .

"I've got to ask, Sara. Haven't you wanted to go out with any of Tammy's candidates, just once, out of curiosity?"

Sara glared at him.

"You've asked me that twice before, Bob, and both times I've told you I'm not the slightest bit interested in anyone but you!" She drew in a sharp breath.

"Don't you believe me? Don't you trust me?"

They stared at each other, and Sara's heart missed a beat. Bob looked so serious! Surely he knew her feelings for him by now?

She'd never thought Bob was the jealous sort. She knew what that was like because of Tim. Much as she'd loved Tim, he hadn't always been easy to live with . . .

"Of course I trust you," Bob said steadily. "It's just that I still find it hard to believe that you really want me. You're so very special, you see . . ."

54

Ducks by Loch Earn, Perthshire.

"Oh, Bob!" Her heart melted. "You're special, too. And, of course I trust you. If we don't trust each other we might as well give up right now!"

He took her hand and kissed it. She got out of the car. Which was how they parted, a bit stiffly, a bit insecure.

PERCHED in the old oak at the end of his drive, Gary watched Sara walk quickly, almost angrily down the road. Dad locked the car and started for the house.

By the way Dad walked, head down, they couldn't have decided to tell him what was going on. They might even have quarrelled.

He'd guessed how Dad felt about Tammy's mum ages ago. He couldn't understand why Tammy hadn't twigged yet.

Any number of times he'd been on the verge of telling, but managed to stop himself. He wasn't at all sure what Tammy's reaction would be to having his dad for a stepfather.

Why had she never once thought of Dad being a possibility for her mum? She didn't seem to see Dad as eligible. Perhaps she didn't like carpenters?

Why was Dad so glum? Had Mrs Morgan decided she liked the optician after all? Gary would never have thought she'd fall in with any of Tammy's lame-duck candidates.

He'd got to do something about it. But what? Gary thought hard.

He didn't want Dad to get hurt, and there was only one way to prevent that happening . . . Gary dropped out of the tree, and went indoors to wash first.

ALL right, Tammy. I accept you meant well, and you want me to have someone 'special for myself', as you put it, for when you leave home.

"But —" Sara paused for breath. Tammy stood with her arms, clasped across her midriff, gazing at the floor.

"Didn't it ever occur to you to *ask* me whether I was interested in getting married again?" Sara burst out.

Tammy shook her head. How could she explain to Mum now that the worry uppermost in her mind had been the house? Mum loved this house so much — the house she and Dad had planned.

It had been obvious to Tammy for ages that Bob and Mum cared for each other, yet they did nothing about it. Perhaps Mum was worried because she thought Tammy was as attached to this house as she was?

They looked at each other, then Tammy's defiant face crumpled, and Sara's annoyance left her.

Next thing, they were hugging each other, and crying a little bit, and Tammy was telling her mother at last exactly why she'd done what she'd done . . .

That was when there was a cautious cough. They turned round.

"Gary!" Sara smiled at him. "Come to see Tammy? Here she is."

But Gary stayed put.

"I came to s-see you, Mrs Morgan, not Tammy," he got out. And as Tammy stared, he added, "It's private, you see?"

Sara swallowed her surprise.

"Better come into the front room, then, Gary."

He followed her into the house, across the wood block floor. Despite his nerves, he couldn't help thinking that it was good workmanship.

"Gary?" Tammy had followed them into the hall.

"See you later, Tam," he said awkwardly.

"You might!" She walked back out of the front door.

Outside, she stood for a moment or two, thinking.

Had Gary finally confided in his dad about what Tammy had been planning? She could quite see that Mr Wainwright would send Gary to tell Mum . . .

Tammy sighed.

"One way to find out," she muttered, and turned to her right.

Gary's dad was standing under the oak tree by his drive. He came to meet her.

"Hello, Tammy. I was just coming to see your mum."

"Gary's beaten you to it," she burst out. "He's at the house right now. Seeing Mum, in private . . ."

Her eyes met Bob's.

"Do you know what it's about?" he asked gently.

She met his steady look and told the truth.

"I expect it's about me finding boyfriends for her —"

Bob shook his head.

"No. It's about your mum and me getting married. Gary approves. What about you?"

Tammy blinked in shock. He waited quietly, relaxed, not seeming at all nervous about her reaction.

"You worked on our house when it was built, didn't you?" she said inconsequentially. "I remember Dad saying that the good woodwork was all your doing.

"I mean, you and Mum have known each other for ages, but what I can't understand was why the two of you didn't get together sooner. You seemed so right, somehow . . ."

"Two reasons, Tammy." He was sitting on the wall now. "Your mum's been worried that you're so attached to your dad's house — you wouldn't want to move." He paused.

"And I've been worried because I thought Gary might be — well, keen on you."

Tammy drew in a deep breath.

"Well, now you know Gary isn't. He must have told you. We're mates.

"And me trying to find someone for Mum should have made her realise *I'm* not too attached to the house." She looked at him.

"And if you ask me, you'd better get on with marrying Mum soon. Just in case one of the others takes her fancy after all!"

Bob laughed. He was about to say he'd never thought of that, when he remembered his last conversation with Sara.

"All I really wanted," Tammy added, "was to get things moving —"

Bob's gaze slipped away over her shoulder, and he smiled. Mum and Gary were walking up the road side by side, Tammy saw.

"You weren't the only one who wanted to get things moving, it appears." Bob put an arm round her shoulders. "That's just what Gary said before he went to see your mum!"

"And now things are moving," Tammy said contentedly.

"Oh, I think you could say they'd moved!" Bob drew her mother close and kissed her.

"How about a barbecue for tea?" he said over his shoulder.

"Yes, please!" Tammy said at once.

Her mum leaned back in Bob's arms and grinned.

"Well, the two of you had better get on with it, then, hadn't you? Get things moving!"

So they did. ❏

Illustration by Mark Viney.

Young At Heart

ANN GARFORTH was up with the sparrows on the morning of her seventieth birthday.

Mrs Johnson, who cleaned for her two days a week, arrived at eight-thirty and proved to be even more irritating than usual. She whisked a handful of post from behind her back like a conjurer producing a rabbit.

"Look what we've got here, Mrs Garforth." After banging the Hoover into two doors, she shouted above the roar of the motor.

"I expect you'll be taking it easy this morning. A nice little rest before the family start arriving."

Ann drew herself up to her full height.

"I'm not a tottering wreck, you know. I'm going to dig the delphiniums out of the flower bed."

Mrs Johnson frowned at her as if she was a naughty child.

Ann looked twenty years younger than her age. Her hair was always neat — and her clothes were chosen with great care. Physically, she was — as she put it — "as strong as a dray horse". She played golf twice a week and joined the local ramblers' club for eight-mile walks at weekends, often outpacing hikers half her age.

She was a grandmother and her large family loved her. They brought all their problems and worries to her and she usually managed to solve them.

"You ought to apply for one of those agony aunt jobs, Mum," her daughter, Ruth, said. "You'd sort the readers out in five seconds flat."

The Hoover thundered into the room and Mrs Johnson's high-pitched voice came across piercingly.

"There's a bitter wind out there you know, Mrs Garforth."

Ann bit her tongue.

"There's nothing wrong with my overcoat, Mrs Johnson," she said briskly.

------ by Mary Kettlewell ------

THE family pilgrimage started at two p.m. First came her son, Phil, and daughter-in-law, Kerry, carrying three cheerfully wrapped bottles.

"Sherry, Mum. That dry sort you like." They also brought with them the first problem of the day.

"Mum, we're thinking of buying a bigger house now Sue is growing up so fast. What do you think?"

"The way prices are going up, you can't lose. And young girls do need their privacy. I think it's a good idea."

Next to turn up were five of her six grandchildren — Johnny, Luke, Sue, Debbie and Fran.

"Hi, Gran. Happy birthday." Kisses and hugs followed and the pile of presents grew steadily higher. And, of course, problems came thick and fast.

"Gran, what shall I wear at the disco tonight? My short blue dress or that green, slinky one?" This was Debbie.

"The blue one, dear." Ann smiled. "It really suits you. The boys will be clustering round like bees near a honeycomb."

She helped Johnny decide whether to take geography or history

A-level, told Luke he was too young to buy a motor-cycle and reassured Fran that she would soon grow taller.

By half past four, the family procession had petered out, leaving the room an Aladdin's Cave. Plants, birthday cake, book tokens, CDs, a new umbrella, a pair of slippers and enough chocolates to feed an army were piled up on the table.

James, her oldest son, had just left when the phone rang.

A burst of crackling came through the receiver, then a distant-sounding voice spoke.

"Gran, it's me — Jack. I've got held up."

It was her eldest grandson.

"Where are you, dear?"

"On the motorway. I can't talk for long. I'm doing seventy."

Ann took a deep breath.

"For heaven's sake get your hands on the wheel and slow down, Jack. I want to see you here in one piece."

"Cheers, Gran. Give me half an hour." And the line went dead.

She smiled. Jack was one of her favourites. A tall boy of eighteen, he was good looking and happy-go-lucky.

Forty minutes later, the door burst open.

"Happy birthday, Gran!" He gave her a smacking kiss on the cheek. "I've bought you a couple of presents." He handed her two roughly packaged parcels.

"Thank you, dear."

The first parcel contained a bristly shoe wiper in the shape of a squashed hedgehog.

"It's a joke, Gran. They're all the rage nowadays."

She didn't tell him she'd been up and down every road in Hitchborough that week, collecting for the Red Cross, and hadn't seen a single squashed hedgehog.

"Just what I wanted, Jack. I was digging yesterday. The garden's inches deep in mud."

Jack whistled through his teeth.

"Digging? You're amazing. You'll get yourself in the Guinness Book of Records at this rate. England's fittest gran!"

The other present proved to be a framed poster of Oor Wullie — her favourite cartoon character.

Ann gave a mischievous smile.

"This cheeky lad will brighten up the room no end."

Jack joined Gran for dinner and was soon confessing he had a new girlfriend.

"We've been going out for ages," he revealed.

"And how long is that?"

"Three weeks."

She smiled to herself.

"We're off to Malta for a week in May," he went on. "We booked cheap tickets on the internet." He smiled dreamily.

"Lynn's gorgeous . . . Do you want to see a photo of her?"

"I'd love to."

He produced a crumpled photograph from his pocket and passed it over. On the bottom, Lynn had scrawled, *Hi, Jack. Dig this mugshot. Lynn.*

Ann felt it lacked the romantic touch. In her day, she would have put love and kisses on a photograph.

The girl had dark eyes, very dark eyebrows and black wavy hair. The curious thing was her skin. It was deadly white.

"She's a lovely girl, Jack, but she looks a bit pale. Do you two get enough fresh air?"

"That's just make-up, Gran. It's part of her look." He put away the snap and then ran a hand wearily through his hair.

"Jack," Ann said carefully, "you're looking tired. Are you all right?"

He gave her a half-hearted smile.

"We had rather a heavy night at the disco. I've still got a bit of a hangover."

He suddenly gave a cheeky grin.

"I suppose with you and Grandad it was all different. Sort of old-fashioned. No night clubs, discos, parties and kissing."

Ann laughed softly.

"I don't think you could call your grandfather and me old-fashioned, Jack. We were hippies in the early Sixties. Will and I backpacked our way all over the world.

"Sat at the feet of a guru in India. Thumbed our way through Afghanistan and got shot at on the Khyber Pass. We even stayed in a Buddhist monastery for three weeks. I've got a picture of us in the Himalayas somewhere."

She stood up and rummaged through her writing desk.

"Here — look."

The photograph showed a young woman with long plaits and tropical flowers in her hair. She was wearing an ankle-length Tibetan robe and sandals. Beside her stood a young man with long hair cascading down his back. His T-shirt said, *Make Love Not War.*

"That's you and Grandad?" Jack gaped.

"Yes, with Mount Everest in the background."

"I can't believe it!" He looked at her with new eyes.

"After that, we went to Australia." Ann was remembering.

The Rose Garden

by Alex Mu

Perfect Planting

FRAGRANT roses are a joy to many gardeners. If you would like to enjoy a rose bush or two, they should be planted before the end of March.

Start by making sure that you have the right planting site for your new bushes and that it is properly prepared.

Roses need plenty of sunshine but some slight shade during the early afternoon can be beneficial. They can't stand deep shade.

An ideal site would be an open, sunny situation, protected from north or east winds.

Roses can be grown in almost any type of soil, as long as it is well drained and has been enriched with plenty of plant foods and humus.

Prepare the site by double digging the area, at the same time working in compost, well-rotted manure, or any other vegetative materials. The top spit should have some rose fertiliser forked in as well, allowing about four ounces to the square yard. If possible, let the soil settle for a week or two before you start planting.

If you're replacing roses in an established bed, you'll have to change the soil. For some reason, the soil becomes "rose sick" when roses have been growing there for years and, as a result, new bushes will never flourish as they should.

Dig out the old soil so that you have a hole about eighteen inches deep and two feet across. Replace it with fresh soil from another part of the garden.

Always give your new bushes a good long drink before you plant them and then dig out a hole which is large enough to let the roots spread out.

To judge the correct planting depth, look for the budding union — the point where the stems emerge from the root stock. When the hole is filled in, this

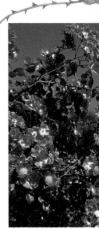

Keep Them Happy

MAKE sure your rose bushes are kept well watered during any long spells of dry weather.

Unless they are growing in sandy soil, most established roses can survive periods of drought, but newly-planted bushes will suffer.

When watering is needed, always be generous. Use a watering-can without a rose and hold the spout close to the ground, allowing about a gallon to each plant.

Newly-planted climbers growing against a wall will need even more water. In long, hot spells of weather even established climbers may need about three gallons of water at each application.

Don't be disappointed if a newly-planted rambling rose fails to flower — they can take some time to settle down.

Other types of roses usually manage to produce some blooms in their first season. If you are tempted to cut a few, take only short pieces of the stems without any leaves.

Even with established bushes you should cut the flowers with care. Always cut above an outward-facing bud and take no more than half the stem.

point should be slightly below the surface of the soil.

Prepare a mixture of moist peat and bonemeal and put this into the hole, shaping it into a slight mound. Set the rose bush on top, spread out the roots evenly and work some fine soil around them. Move the plant gently up and down so that the soil can filter between the roots.

Half-fill the hole, then firm down the soil with gentle treading. Add more soil until the hole is full, then tread it down once again. Water in well.

"We hired a motor-bike down in Adelaide and did the most crazy thing. Rode six hundred miles to Alice Springs on a desert road with no crash helmets in a temperature of one hundred and twenty degrees." She giggled at the memory.

"It was a powerful machine — a Norton. It took us three days and we arrived covered in flies and dust!"

Jack stared at her, lost for words.

"The best part was Ayers Rock. We climbed up and, as the sun rose, Will proposed to me. It was incredible!" Ann laughed softly. "But, on the way down, he fell and hurt his leg. And I had to get us back to Alice."

Jack looked as if he had been hit with a sledge hammer.

"You mean you drove a Norton motorbike?"

"Yes, dear. With your grandad riding pillion. We touched eighty miles an hour. It was one of the best moments of my life."

Later, while they were washing-up, Jack looked at Ann thoughtfully.

"Gran, did the two of you ever have rows when you were courting?"

"Frequently, darling. I remember, one day, your grandpa had gone out to celebrate his football club winning some trophy. He didn't get home until three in the morning. He was *supposed* to have been back in time to take me out for a birthday meal."

"What happened?"

"I despatched him to the dog house and refused to speak to him."

"What did he do?"

"Wrote me a pile of love letters. And, when I still wouldn't speak to him, he paid me a midnight visit.

"I was in bed when I heard a tapping noise at the window." She laughed at the memory. "D'you know what he'd done? He'd bought the biggest bunch of flowers he could find, borrowed a ladder from the garage and climbed up to my window!"

Jack was silent for a long moment.

"Gran . . .? He looked awkward for a moment. "I've fallen out with Lynn. You see, at the disco last night I started dancing with another girl and she kissed me." He took a deep breath. "It didn't mean anything, but Lynn got the wrong idea."

Ann shook her head.

"Maybe you shouldn't have been dancing with another girl. Tell Lynn you're sorry."

"I tried that after the disco, but she didn't want to talk to me."

"What did you say?"

He looked sheepish.

"I asked her if she fancied a take-away."

Ann shook her head.

"No wonder she didn't listen! You should explain and apologise. Tell her she means more to you than all the world."

"And that'll do the trick?" He looked hopeful.

"I don't know the girl," she said cautiously. "But most people like to feel loved and wanted. Take her flowers and write her a love letter. It may work."

His face lit up.

"That's a great idea! I'll just have time, if I rush. That shop at the station stays open till eleven." He hurried into his jacket, thrusting a hand into his pocket.

"Oh, no . . . I've . . ."

"No money," Ann guessed, fishing in her handbag. "Here — it's on me."

"Thanks, Gran."

"Bring her to see me if you're successful, Jack, dear."

S HE was out pruning the roses the following morning when a car drew up with a squeal. Jack sprung out and she guessed from his smile that all was well.

The passenger door opened and a familiar figure climbed out. In the light of day, Lynn looked pretty and very young.

"Gran, I've brought Lynn round before we go back to Liverpool."

"Come on in, both of you. I'll put the kettle on."

Jack kept up a running commentary on Lynn's attributes as Ann bustled around preparing the tea.

"She's top in her year for geography. And she won a prize for clothes design."

"I was just admiring your waistcoat, Lynn. Did you make it?"

She nodded shyly.

"With a bit of help from my mum and some embroidery lessons."

Soon the ice was broken and they were chatting easily.

When Jack went out to the garden to refill Ann's log box, Lynn confided in her.

"You'll never guess what Jack did. We had a stupid row two nights ago. And do you know what he did? He bought an enormous bunch of roses. Goodness only knows what they cost!"

Ann smiled wryly to herself.

"He got a ladder out of my dad's shed and put it up to my window so he could give me the flowers." Her eyes were shining.

"What a lovely way to make up."

"He wrote me a love letter, too." She sighed.

Half an hour later, Ann waved them off and picked up the secateurs to finish the rose pruning. It had been quite a birthday! Parcels piled high as the ceiling. All her lovely family to see her. A host of problems sorted out. Young Jack and his Lynn reunited. And, best of all, the chance to relive the heady, hectic days when she had been a young girl driving a Norton over the Australian Outback with her fiancé riding pillion behind.

When twilight fell, she went inside and hung the cheeky Oor Wullie picture up.

She could hardly wait to see Mrs Johnson's face next morning! ❏

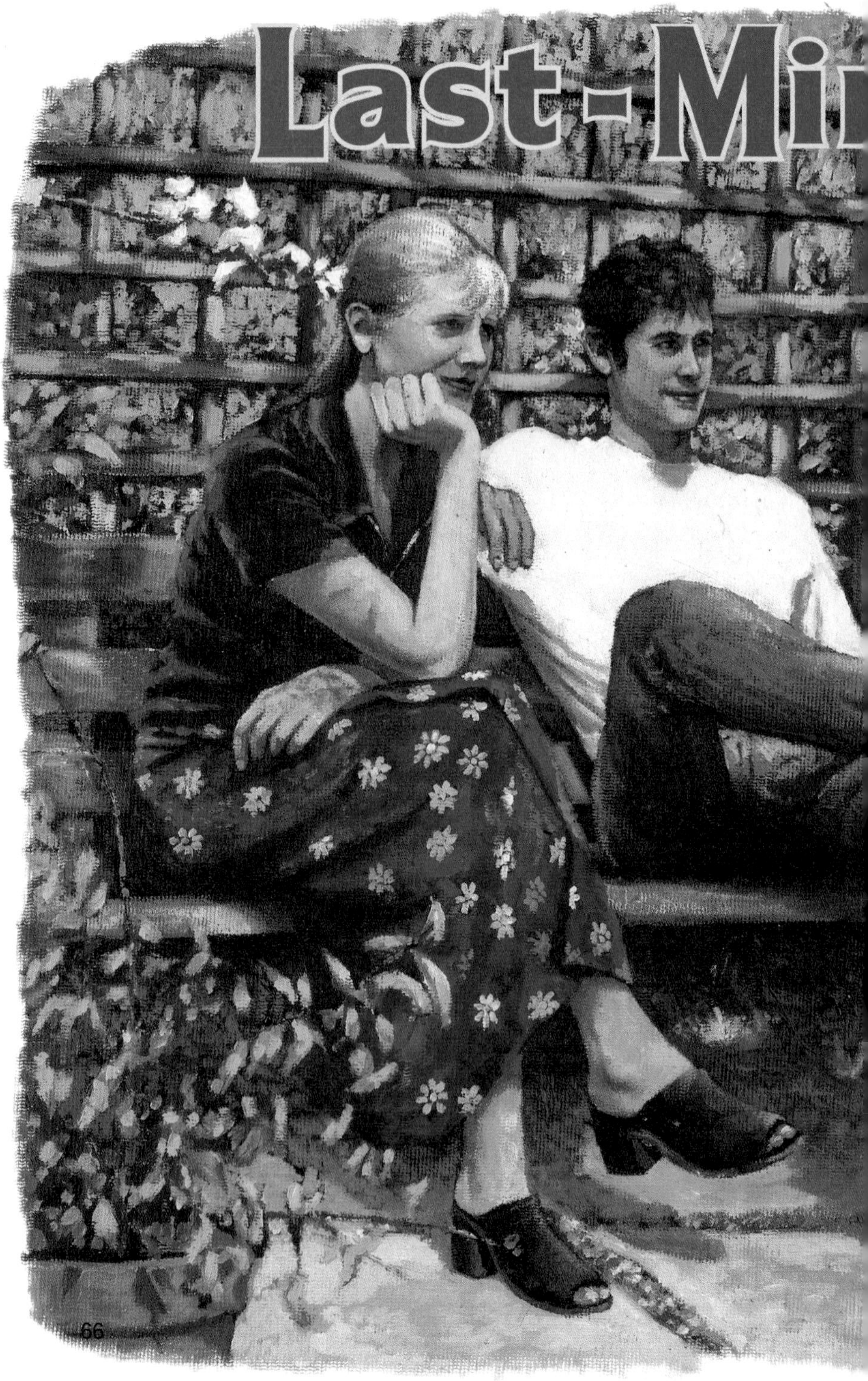
Last-Mi

ite Nerves

KEEP that," Patrick said. "It's a seedling. Look, there are several of them."

With a flick of her trowel, Ginnie uprooted the seedling, exposing its fragile white roots to the air, and dropped it into the bucket beside her.

"Ginnie," Patrick said slowly, sitting back on his haunches. "What's wrong? Why did you do that? You're not happy, are you?"

Ginnie kept her head down. No, she wasn't happy. But she couldn't tell Patrick why, because she wasn't sure herself.

"It's just, you know, I think the pressure is getting to me."

"Well, it shouldn't be. Please try to relax."

Ginnie felt tears at the back of her eyes but refused to cry. She'd promised to help Patrick tidy his garden and she didn't want to let him down.

"I reckon you need a cuppa," Patrick said, jumping up.

Ginnie watched him walk to the house. Patrick always seemed so sure. Why couldn't she be?

She sat back on the newly turned earth and looked at the bed they'd worked over. They were almost finished. Once the grass was cut and the edges neatened, they could get in touch with the estate

**by
Judith
Davis**

Illustration by David Young.

agents and the house could be put up for sale.

Ginnie gazed up at the pale blue of the summer sky and felt a sudden longing to get away — from the garden, the decorating, the preparations for the wedding . . . But mostly from Patrick . . .

This last thought shocked her and she turned her attention to weeding again, trowelling down to reach the deep root of a dandelion. She dug hard and took hold of the plant in her gloved hand, pulling it.

It came up suddenly, the root end snapping off. She knew that the dandelion would sprout again, but by then the house might be sold and she and Patrick would be living at Hazelcroft.

That was enough. She threw down the trowel, pulled off her gloves and stood up, her heart pounding. Patting her pocket to check for the car keys she set off at a run for her car, parked next to Patrick's Land-Rover.

In the rear-view mirror, as she drove away, she saw Patrick emerge from the house, a cup in each hand. He stared after her.

She felt bad, deserting him, but she needed to be alone. Somehow, lately, she never seemed to be alone.

She couldn't understand why she was feeling so anxious. It wasn't as if she had agreed to marry Patrick without serious forethought. They were not youngsters. Both were in their thirties with careers and experience behind them.

They had been childhood friends but it was only in the past twelve months that both had found within the other something deeper than friendship, and Ginnie had been overjoyed when Patrick proposed. It was only later that doubts began to surface . . .

GINNIE slowed for a set of traffic lights. Now these doubts seemed to overwhelm everything save for the fact that she still loved Patrick. What was the matter with her? Why, now that she had finally made the decision to get married, did everything seem to be getting on top of her?

She pulled into the drive at Hazelcroft and jumped out. But, as she was putting the key in the lock, she realised that this was the first place that Patrick would look for her, and she felt she couldn't face him just now.

She turned, hurrying past the car, heading for the path which led to the dunes. There she knew she could hide away, and hopefully walk off some of her anxiety.

She was soon making her way along the narrow pathway between the houses, the quickest way to the beach. Behind her, in the distance, she thought she heard the roar of Patrick's Land-Rover and hurried her step.

Soon she was walking between the tall mounds where marram grass waved in the strong breeze and the sand was soft and slippery underfoot.

"Hello, there."

"'Morning, Molly." Ginnie managed a forced smile.

"Didn't expect to see you here. Thought you'd be hard at work at young Patrick's place."

"I felt like a blow on the beach." Ginnie smiled, wishing she had the nerve to be rude and walk on.

Molly Cooper eased the bundle of driftwood under her arm.

"Like that, is it? Cold feet?"

Ginnie was taken aback by Molly's cheek — and her perception.

"No, I — er . . ."

"Go on, confess it." Molly chuckled. "I got cold feet when I got my only proposal. Told the feller where to go. Said I didn't want to be beholden to anyone."

"Did you, really?" Ginnie was astonished. Molly Cooper, pillar of the local church, ex-Sunday School teacher and WI chairwoman, had always seemed a born spinster.

"It must have been a long time ago," Ginnie said without thinking, then coloured. "Sorry, that just slipped out."

"Oh, it was." Molly laughed. "Donkey's years, I'd say." She yanked again at the driftwood which was rapidly slipping from her grasp.

"Would you mind carrying some of this to my woodshed? It's not far."

Ginnie was about to decline, but something in Molly's faded blue eyes made her decide that to help someone else might at least take her mind off her own troubles.

"Of course. Goodness, you've collected a lot. Do you really burn it all?"

"Absolutely. Couldn't keep warm without it in the winter. Coal's such a price."

Molly led the way to a gate enclosed in a high wall. The gate creaked alarmingly and as Molly banged it shut a few slivers of wood fell away.

"Need a new gate, of course. Have done for years. Dare say it will last me out," Molly declared, striding ahead with her bundle.

"Here we are, just drop it down. I'll stack it later."

Ginnie did as she was bidden, taking note of the tidy wood pile under a sloping lean-to roof. The rest of the back garden was not so neat with straggly grass and thick nettles near the back wall. Only one bed near the house looked cultivated — a lush jumble of feathery fronds and assorted leaves which gave off a pungent scent as they brushed past.

"My herbs," Molly said proudly. "Rheumatics have put paid to most of my gardening, but I wouldn't be without my herbs. Can't cook without herbs, can you?"

Ginnie murmured politely, though in her case she hardly ever thought of herbs, save to put mint with new potatoes.

"Oh, what a wonderful smell," Ginnie breathed, as Molly ushered her into the kitchen,

"Chicken broth, flavoured with sage, parsley, fennel, thyme and a little rosemary," Molly said, reaching for the kettle and filling it briskly. "Makes a silk purse out of a sow's ear of a boiling fowl."

Ginnie smiled politely. What was she doing talking about herbs with Mad Molly when she could have been tramping out along the beach trying to sort out this muddle in her mind?

Ginnie flushed, and was glad that Molly was busy setting mugs on a tray. Why had that particular childish nickname suddenly reared its head?

Poor Molly. She was clearly no madder than anyone else but, when she'd taken the Sunday school class, the children had all called her Mad Molly behind her back.

"So, what's the trouble then, my dear? Don't you think Patrick's the man for you?"

Ginnie sat at a table littered with books, a cereal packet and several empty jam jars. She nodded thanks as Molly poured her out a steaming mug of tea.

"It's not that at all. Patrick, I'm sure of. I'm not so sure of myself."

"I see." Molly opened a biscuit tin and dug inside it. "You might find a whole one here, if you're lucky. Yes, here we are." She fished out a crumby digestive and held it up. "The rest are shattered, I'm afraid. D'you want it?"

Ginnie shook her head, suddenly reminded of how Molly had earned her nickname. Molly used to regularly reward the Sunday School pupils with broken biscuits. They were a speciality of her local grocer's in those days.

Now, of course, no-one would buy a biscuit knowing it was broken. But, back then, those who were well acquainted with their Bible stories and could trot out the answers to Molly's questions would be showered, sometimes literally, with biscuit fragments.

Ginnie felt like reminding Molly of this memory but decided it might not be tactful. However, she shook her head at the offer of a biscuit.

"No thanks." She smiled. "I'm trying to keep off them . . ."

"For the big day." Molly nodded intuitively, finishing her sentence.

Crail, Fife

SINCE the charter of 1178, Crail has been a royal burgh — which makes it one of the oldest in Scotland.

It was fishing and trade with the Netherlands, France and Scandinavia which encouraged the growth of this popular little town. And Dutch influence can still be seen today in the distinctive architecture of the houses which look down on the narrow harbour mouth.

There was, in fact, a two-way influence as trade flourished, and you can find Scottish-style homes in Holland!

Artists and tourists alike love Crail, with its quaint streets and harbour, and stunning sea views.

CRAIL, FIFE: J CAMPBELL KERR

71

"Good heavens, girl, you don't need to lose weight. If Patrick had wanted a skinny beanpole to marry he would have chosen someone else. You've got a lovely figure."

Ginnie's shoulders slumped. She didn't mind Molly's bracing remarks. She was hardly listening.

She cupped her hands around the mug and sipped at the tea, trying to divert herself from the feeling that any minute she was going to dissolve in tears and disgrace herself.

Molly didn't seem to notice. She briskly stirred several spoonfuls of sugar into her own mug and chomped happily on the biscuit.

"Yes, I was a fool, I suppose, looking back. He was a perfectly good chap. Quite presentable, in his own way, though he looked like a turtle as he got older. I used to see him sometimes, when he came to functions in the village with his wife."

Ginnie blinked back her tears. What was Molly talking about?

"Rich as Croesus, too, in later life. His father made a mint on something or other and left it all to old Roddy." Molly fished in the tin for another piece of biscuit. "I'd have been quite well off."

She grinned and gestured with a biscuit fragment.

"So, let that be a lesson to you, Ginnie, my girl. Take it from an old bird who knows. Maintaining your independence is all very well, but marriage could very well be a better deal."

Ginnie slowly sipped her mug of tea. The strength of it, and the slightly odd taste, was soothing.

"Camomile, mixed with ordinary tea leaves. It's my calming brew. Like it?"

"I do." Ginnie grinned. "Thanks."

She heaved a sigh.

"Yes, I do feel a little better. I don't know what came over me. Poor Patrick, he must be wondering where on earth I've gone."

"Not if he has any sense, and I fancy he has. Everyone needs their own space, as they say nowadays. Especially when you've got the most important day of your life coming up. You need to be sure, my dear. If you're not, tell him. He'll understand."

"But will he?" Ginnie wondered sadly. "I thought I wanted to be married. I do love Patrick. When I don't see him I feel miserable. But I have this silly feeling . . . I know it's irrational, and selfish, but . . ."

She shook her head.

"I shouldn't be burdening you with my troubles."

Molly leaned across the table and looked intently at Ginnie.

"I'll tell you this, my girl, you don't look as bright as a prospective bride should. Don't let yourself be railroaded into marriage. Better end up a batty old spinster like me than that!"

Molly shook with laughter and Ginnie looked gratefully at her.

"You know, you're the first person who's said anything like that to me." She spread her hands expressively. "You're quite right about railroading. Lately I've felt as though I'm on an express, speeding towards a tunnel, with no brakes."

"There are always brakes, my dear. But make sure you put them on for the right reason. Let's see now. You say you love Patrick?"

"I do," Ginnie said simply. "I can't think of life without him."

"So what's the problem?"

"I think —" her voice was low and slow "— that I'm frightened of committing myself."

She looked at Molly defensively.

"I've not told anyone that. And I can't live at Hazelcroft with Patrick."

"But, my dear, it's a lovely house, and you're both very fortunate to have a house each."

"I know," Ginnie said, flushing. "If we were just starting out in our twenties it would be different. But we're not. Hazelcroft is *my* home, and Patrick's house is so much his."

Molly looked taken aback.

"So what do you propose? Living in two separate houses? It doesn't seem a very good start to marriage."

"No, of course not."

"No-one can have their cake and eat it, too. It just isn't cricket."

GINNIE flushed. No-one but Mad Molly would have said that to her. But it was true. She did want her cake and to be able to eat it, too. She wanted Patrick, for she loved him dearly. But she felt this awful apprehension about letting go of her independence. She was frightened, too, that she wouldn't live up to Patrick's expectations.

"It will work," Molly said softly. "I've seen you two together. You're right for one another. And it doesn't matter a hang where you live."

She jumped up.

"Right, now I must chivvy you off. I've got things to do. People to visit." She began to put the empty jam jars into a carrier bag. "I'm taking these to the WI stall in the village hall. Are you walking my way?"

"No, I must get back to Patrick. We've still got a garden to finish."

Molly put her hand on Ginnie's arm as she showed her out.

"Tell him. Whatever it is. Patrick will understand. Tell him you want to elope to Gretna and forget the fuss. Why not?" Molly's shout of laughter echoed in Ginnie's head as she hurried past the herb bed to the back gate.

"About time, too," Patrick murmured, smiling, as she pulled the rickety gate shut. He was leaning against Molly's sunsplashed back wall, his hands in his pockets.

"Patrick!" Ginnie jumped guiltily. "How did you know I was here?"

"I haven't been a Boy Scout for nothing." He nodded towards her boots. "I'd know your welly footsteps anywhere."

Ginnie stood on one leg to look at her ridged and patterned sole and the distinctive footstep it left on the sandy path.

"Well, you are clever," she said, her eyes adroitly avoiding his.

"We're going for a walk." Patrick took her hand, gently but firmly.

"But the garden . . . We've got so little time . . ."

"We've got all the time in the world," Patrick said quietly. "And the garden doesn't matter. Nothing matters, except you and me."

Ginnie stole a look at him, but his eyes were ahead, and she was glad that he didn't seem to expect any response.

They walked past the piled-up dunes and out on to the wide open beach. The sea glinted, overhead sea birds swooped and called and in front of them the tide swooshed in and out.

Patrick stopped suddenly, swinging Ginnie round and taking her in his arms.

"Now tell me, my love, do you still, honestly, want to marry me?"

Ginnie felt the warmth of his encircling embrace against the keen breeze from the sea.

"Yes, I do," she whispered, leaning against him.

She looked up at him and remembered what Molly had said.

"I think we should sell both houses and start afresh."

A mix of expressions chased across Patrick's face.

"But I thought you loved Hazelcroft?"

"I do. I love it too much. I associate Hazelcroft with every childhood tantrum and always getting my own way. My parents were indulgent, you know that." She looked up at Patrick's face and raised a hand to caress his cheek.

"I've always been selfish, afraid of committing myself, of losing my independence. But, more than that, I think I've been afraid of growing up."

Patrick's eyes widened. He smiled and seemed about to speak, but Ginnie put her fingers gently on his lips.

"It isn't just a whim, my love, and I know it seems ridiculously wasteful when we've got two houses already, but I think our marriage deserves a fresh start. Do you mind?"

Patrick looked at her with eyes so full of love that Ginnie wondered how she had ever doubted anything.

"Ginnie, darling, a few minutes ago I thought you were going to back out on me. If it would make you happy, I'd live with you in a dustbin."

Ginnie exhaled a great sigh and snuggled into his jacket.

"There, I've said all that's been worrying me for weeks. If you'll still have me now then you deserve all you get."

Patrick spoke over her head, and his words were interspersed by the sea birds' cries, and the never-ending movement of the sea.

"What I'm getting, Ginnie, is a real grown-up woman, and I can't wait for you to be my wife." Then, very tenderly, he raised her face to his. ❑

74

Illustration by Gerard Fay.

by Jennie Peel

Keep Mum!

HAVE you ever wished you hadn't posted something as soon as you've dropped it into the depths of the post-box? No sooner had it left my hand, than I wished I hadn't let go of that card.

What if James found out? My husband is a kind man — rather lacking in romance and imagination, but he does try to understand when my impulses overcome me. But he did hate me to "interfere" . . .

Of course, there was no reason to suppose that he would find out, I consoled myself. After all, no-one could ever be completely sure of the source of an unsigned Valentine card.

Half an hour later, I was in the kitchen, engulfed in the domesticity of meal preparation — all thoughts of Valentine cards put firmly to one side.

"I won't want anything to eat," Lucy announced, as soon as she was through the back door.

"How was school?" I asked, ignoring her comment.

I could have saved my breath. She was gone. Her bedroom door slammed and, within minutes, a mournful ballad wafted through the house.

Then there was a crash and two filthy, wet figures burst through the back door and collapsed in a heap of muddy boots and tangled rucksacks.

Why is it, I wondered for the millionth time, that teenage boys always have to have such unbelievably large bags for school? They certainly don't carry all their school books in them. Charlie's text books are usually tangled in a pile of mouldering socks and assorted T-shirts under his bed.

I'VE said Ben can stay for tea. That OK?" he asked.

Uncharacteristically, I refrained from saying the first words that sprung to my lips.

"Fine, Charlie. But get tidied up now."

"But, Mum . . ."

"Now!"

"Yes, Mrs Hunt. Thank you," Ben said, flashing a smile that I suspected was reserved for teachers and mothers.

"Oh, no." Charlie groaned, rolling his eyes heavenwards as he became aware of the melancholy music. "Lucy's not still moping over Craig, is she?"

"No idea," I lied. "Get washed."

"OK, OK. Chill out, Mum. We're going."

The boys whirled out of the kitchen like Hurricane Harry, and I was left to my thoughts.

Perhaps Lucy would feel a bit more cheerful tomorrow.

It had been so much easier to solve her problems when she was younger and chatted away about everything. She didn't talk to me now. She probably thought I wouldn't understand how she felt, but I understood all too well. It doesn't matter what age you are, if you love someone more than they love you, heartbreak hurts just as much.

James was always giving me endless lectures about not interfering in her life. I didn't want to interfere, just help, but he could never see the difference.

T. Parker.

Baby Donkey

WITH floppy ears and furry face,
He's loved for his appealing ways,
A member of an ancient race
And friend of man from early days.

He'll go where horses cannot tread,
Along the cloudy mountain trail,
Up cobbled streets his way he'll thread
With small, sure steps that never fail.

With childhood memories he blends —
Those donkey rides in warm sea air!
The postcards that we sent to friends
To make them wish that they were there!

On Christmas cards he's much in view,
Of humble beasts he wears the crown
And he was in the stable, too,
When heaven's light to earth came down.
— *Brenda G. Macrow.*

"Can we, Mum?"

My son brought me back to earth.

"Sorry, Charlie, what was that?"

"I was just asking," Charlie said, in his I'm-being-so-patient-with-this-idiot voice, "whether Ben and I can have tea in my room."

"OK," I said. I really didn't feel up to the barrage of Charlie's wheedling tactics this afternoon. I had far more important things to think about.

"Thanks, Mum!" Charlie yelled, and disappeared before I could change my mind.

Before I could start daydreaming again, the phone rang.

"I'll be a bit late." It was James. "The trains all seem to be delayed this evening."

I managed to suppress my gratitude to the train company and be suitably sympathetic. James always sounded surprised that the trains wouldn't be arriving when scheduled, although it happened at least once or twice a week.

On this occasion, I was relieved that there would be less time for the inadvertent mention of Valentine cards.

THE next morning, on the top of an unusually large pile of post, I was surprised to see an envelope addressed to me. It looked like a card! Hastily, I picked up the pile and shoved my envelope underneath the rest. I would open it later — once the rest of the family had received their mail.

When Lucy saw three interesting looking envelopes for her, she almost smiled.

She tucked them into her bag and took off through the back door, before I could remind her of the importance of a good breakfast. I sent up a silent prayer that something in one of those envelopes would cheer her up.

"Any post for Lucy?" James asked, shaking the four remaining cornflakes into his bowl.

"Why?"

"Oh, no reason."

Poor James, he's such a hopeless liar. He had never, as far as I could remember, ever asked a question without having a reason. As he sat staring intently at his cornflakes, his face took on a decidedly rosy hue. I decided not to tease him.

"Yes, three things that could be Valentines."

"Splendid," James said, going an even deeper shade of pink. "Any other interesting post?"

He picked up the pile, which I snatched from him.

"I haven't had a chance to look yet," I lied.

Should I "discover" my envelope now? After all, it might be a birthday card from daft Aunt Joan — two months early. Curiosity overcame me.

"Oh, look," I said casually, tearing open my envelope. Inside was the sort of Valentine card I would have chosen myself, had I been sending me one. It was unsigned.

"It seems I have an admirer." I laughed, delighted.

"That's nice." James didn't even look up. "Oh, no, is that the time?" And he rushed out before I had a chance to thank him for the card.

I was left feeling rather non-plussed. Surely he must have sent the card? Yet, it had been years since he'd remembered Valentine's Day. Maybe I did have a secret admirer . . .

I COULDN'T wait for Lucy to get home that afternoon to find out if the Valentines had cheered her up. She appeared only briefly. "Going to the cinema. I'll get a burger or something," she imparted on her way through the kitchen. However, I had time to notice a smile which none of us had seen for quite a while.

"Well, Ben's card did the trick for loopy Lucy," Charlie announced at suppertime.

"What!" James and I exclaimed together.

"Yeah, he reckoned if she got a Valentine's card, she'd stop moping and being such a pain."

"As I'm always telling your mother," James said, "you really shouldn't interfere. Suppose she finds out? She'll be even more upset."

"There's no way she'll find out. It could've been from anyone. Who's yours from Mum?" He winked cheekily.

"It was from me of course," James said quickly, going rather pink again.

"It looked like the sort of thing you like," he went on rather awkwardly. "I saw it when I was getting one for . . ." He stopped and we both stared at him, amazed.

"I know I shouldn't have, but . . ."

"James — what have you done?" Yet I had already guessed.

"I sent Lucy a card."

"Nice one, Dad."

"I don't believe it! After all you've said about not interfering!" I exclaimed, relieved and cross at the same time.

"I know, but she's been so miserable, and she's such a lovely girl. I thought it might help . . . You won't tell her, will you?"

After Charlie and I had stopped laughing at his woebegone face, I gave him a big hug, and we assured him that his secret was safe.

"I've just had a thought," James said, suddenly. "There's still one of Lucy's cards unaccounted for."

"I wonder if it was from Craig, after all," Charlie mused.

"I wonder," I said, not ready to admit to anything! ❏

by Sandy Simpson

The FIRST BORN

GINA was up and out of bed before she'd even had time to open her eyes properly.

Babies did that to you, she'd quickly discovered. One short squawk in the wee small hours was enough to activate a mother's antennae.

Pushing her feet into slippers and struggling with the tie on her dressing-gown, she padded next door into the nursery. The baby was snuffling and shuffling and sucking his fist as if he hadn't seen food for weeks. He didn't look too pleased.

"You're a greedy little boy," Gina whispered, lifting her son into her arms and carrying him over to the basket chair. It was barely three hours since his last feed. Now, the church clock was striking four and she was having to go through the ritual once more.

Cradling him in her left arm, she stroked his plump, smooth cheek as he guzzled hungrily. He was six weeks old. Sometimes she felt as if she'd known him all her life. Sometimes she had to concentrate really hard to remember what life had been like before he came along.

Not that she would change places with anyone. She and Mark had waited a long

81

time for this baby. But years of working in the bank did nothing to prepare you for motherhood . . .

Gina smiled as she recalled trudging home from work to prepare their evening meal and catch up on household chores. She used to complain of feeling tired. Pre-baby days, when they had enjoyed a social life, she used to be exhausted after a late night with friends.

But nothing compared with how she felt nowadays . . .

When did I last have a full night's sleep, she wondered, closing her eyes.

In the last few weeks of her pregnancy, the baby had kept her awake half the night by kicking and punching and doing what had felt like complete somersaults in her tummy!

Since his birth, she'd spent every waking hour feeding or bathing or changing nappies — and stuffing an endless supply of baby clothes into the washing machine.

The health visitor had assured Gina that the night-time feeds wouldn't last for ever.

"By the time he's four months old, you should be able to put him down last thing at night and not hear him until about six — or seven o'clock — if you're lucky," she'd said cheerfully.

But that was months away . . .

Opening her gritty eyes, Gina found that her son had fallen asleep. Lifting him gently on to her shoulder, she gave his little back a rub and immediately he was awake and demanding more food. Cradling him in her right arm, she watched him start to feed again.

MOTHERHOOD was a completely unknown factor! Nobody warned you what it was *really* like.

When she'd announced she was pregnant, everyone had joked about sleepless nights and waving goodbye to long lies on a Sunday morning.

But the reality was no joke! Caring for babies was hard work and sometimes lonely. She wouldn't dare tell Mark, but she missed her old friends from the bank.

She had gone there the previous week to show off her new son. But she'd felt curiously depressed when she'd left. It was as if time had stood still at the bank. Nothing had changed. Still the same gossiping and laughter and complaints.

But Gina had felt distanced from it all, as if she had never been part of the team. Motherhood changed everything.

Her mother had assured her she would make new friends.

"You'll meet other young mums at the baby clinic and at the mother and toddler group," she'd said. "When you were small, my life was a constant round of coffee mornings and kiddies' parties."

Gina hadn't liked to say that times had changed in thirty years. Most of the mothers went back to work, so they didn't have time for parties or coffee mornings.

But, to her surprise, when she'd taken the baby out in the pram that week, she'd stopped to chat to another young woman pushing a toddler in a buggy. They'd compared notes and promised to get together for coffee.

But, when Gina reached home, she'd realised she'd forgotten to ask the other mum for her name and telephone number. She was so tired her brain seemed unable to function beyond the next feed and nappy change!

The baby stopped feeding for a moment and gazed up at her with big blue eyes.

"Oh, I love you," she breathed, her heart lurching with the intensity of mother love. It was wrong to think all these negative thoughts when her son was beautiful and healthy. But she was so tired . . .

Laying him down on the changing mat, she undid the poppers on his sleepsuit, removed his damp nappy and replaced it with a dry one.

"Does that feel better?"

The baby kicked his legs and waved his arms with delight. He looked very pleased with himself and horribly wide awake. Wrapping him tightly in his shawl, she lifted him into her arms and began to rock him.

It was dark outside and although they were almost entering the month of April, she saw that it had snowed in the night.

In the orange glow from the street lights, the snow shimmered and sparkled on rooftops and gardens. It blanketed the fields beyond the village. It blanketed the roads and pavements.

"We're the only two people who know about the snow," she murmured, rocking the baby back and forth, back and forth. "Everyone else is sound asleep." He gurgled happily in response.

The books gave the impression that once you'd fed and changed your baby, it was just a matter of putting them down to sleep. Gina kissed his soft hair. They didn't tell you that newborn babies loved to be talked to and played with and sung to — at all hours of the day and night.

Neither did they advise young mothers how to survive on a few hours of snatched sleep . . .

In the room next door she heard Mark turn over and give a little sigh of contentment. Gina longed to snuggle close to his warm body but she would have to be patient. That was something else that motherhood had taught her.

"Your mum is a very patient lady," she told the baby. "Do I ever give you a row for keeping me awake for hours on end?"

He gave her a funny lop-sided smile which made her heart contract with love again. But his eyes were growing heavy and she laid him back in his cradle and stroked his forehead, over and over again.

Gina found she was holding her breath. Was he asleep? Could she go back to bed? Please fall asleep, she begged, stepping backwards oh so quietly.

Just as she reached the door, he opened his eyes to slits and Gina froze. But all was quiet, save for the sound of the church clock striking five . . .

GINA awoke from a deep and dreamless sleep and reached for Mark. His side of the bed was empty and cold. The radio was playing downstairs. She peered at the alarm clock. It was nine o'clock!

"The baby!"

"He's just wakened up. I'll see to him." Mark smiled, holding a tray and waiting until she was sitting upright before resting it on her knees. "Breakfast is served, my darling."

Gina was speechless. He'd cooked sausages, bacon, eggs and mushrooms. The toast was cut into triangles. The coffee was piping hot. A single red rose had been laid, decoratively, across a large white envelope.

The baby gave an angry yell from the nursery and Mark rolled his eyes.

"I'll fetch him. Enjoy your breakfast. He can wait a few minutes."

Gina savoured her first sip of coffee that day. She couldn't remember the last time she'd sat down to a full breakfast. She couldn't remember the last time she'd sat down to a full meal! Every time she tried to cook something special for Mark and herself, the baby interrupted them . . .

Taking a bite of toast, she opened the envelope and found there was a card inside.

Happy Mother's Day to the World's Best Mum.

Tears filled her eyes. She'd never had a Mother's Day card before. Mark had written, *Love and Kisses, from the two men in your life XXXX.*

The tears rolled down her cheeks.

"Gina? What's wrong?" Mark asked, depositing the disgruntled baby beside her on the bed and putting an arm about her.

"I'm so happy." She wept.

"I had to get up twice in the night and I was tired and feeling sorry for myself but it doesn't matter now. I'm so happy! And my brain has been like porridge recently and I'd forgotten all about Mother's Day, but you didn't forget . . ."

Mark laughed softly and kissed her.

"As if we'd forget the most important day in a mother's calendar. And talking of porridge, eat your breakfast before it gets cold — Mum."

She laughed and wiped her tears. Mother's Day! She hadn't realised, until now, just how important it was.

She felt loved and appreciated and needed. And, although the baby was bawling loudly for attention, suddenly she didn't feel in the least bit tired any more. ❏

YOU could say one good thing about a football match, Kirsty decided as she headed up the concrete steps at half time — it was the one place on earth where the queue for the ladies was always shorter than the one for the gents!

Of course, most women didn't throng to football matches. Most women had more sense! They spent Saturday afternoons shopping, or gossiping, or getting ready for an evening out. At a pinch, they'd be doing the vacuuming or catching up with the ironing. At least they'd be warm and dry, with the biscuit tin within easy reach.

Most women would have refused point blank to go to a football match on a wet February afternoon — but not her.

Kirsty was in love with a man whose idea of a great date was a trip to the match.

Nick had promised to make this day special for her and she'd been idiot enough to believe him. She hadn't realised his idea of "special" was watching his team getting thrashed yet again.

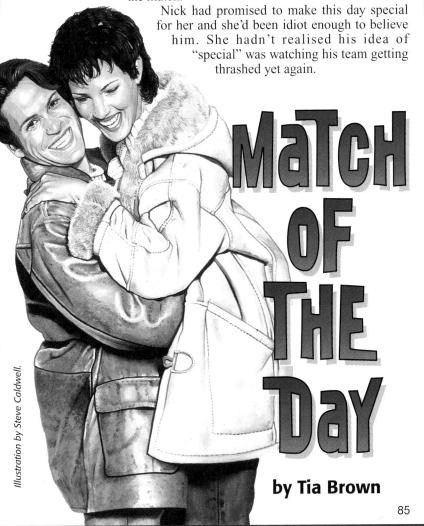

Illustration by Steve Caldwell.

MATCH OF THE DAY

by Tia Brown

If she had any sense, she'd walk out right now. Dump him. Find someone who was more interested in her than football . . . Or even someone who supported a team like Manchester United from the comfort of his armchair. Or maybe, wonderful thought, she might find a man who didn't like football at all!

If she had any sense, she wouldn't stick with Nick, who lived for this obscure team whose greatest ambition, which didn't look like being fulfilled, was to get into the third division.

But she didn't have any sense. She loved him. She told herself she'd rather be here with Nick, despite the weather, than anywhere else . . .

At least, she'd thought that when they'd arrived. Now she wasn't so sure.

She washed her hands then held them under the hot air dryer. Her fingers stung as they thawed out. She looked miserably at her reflection. At least she matched his team colours — red nose and cold-whitened skin. And her hair was all tangled by the wind.

Not that it mattered. Nick wouldn't notice. He never did, which was nice in a way because it meant she could slob around if she wanted to. But then it would be nice if he paid her some attention . . .

"Oh, Kirsty!" she muttered. "You really are an idiot! You want romance, and where are you celebrating your anniversary? At the football!"

Nick had promised that today was going to be different. Well, she decided, reluctantly taking her hands away from the stream of warm air, it was going to be different all right.

She'd tell him that this was the last football match she was coming to. She'd tell him that there was more to life than football. Maybe she'd even suggest he got a life, come to that!

Oh, yes, there was a lot she was going to tell him, but not here. Not when she'd be surrounded by football-mad men. She'd talk to him once they left.

Yet she knew, in her heart of hearts, that she probably wouldn't speak out at all. Once they were clear of here, she'd remember why she loved him, and it would all be fine until the next match.

YOU'VE been ages," he said as she returned to her seat. "I was cold," she said pointedly, giving him one last chance, "and wet, and miserable."

"Oh."

She hadn't expected instant concern, let alone the suggestion that they go home and miss the all-important second half. But she had hoped for more of a response.

"Nick," she said, her voice as cold as the weather, "I really am not enjoying myself."

"But it's only half-time. It'll get better." He was studying the electronic scoreboard which was currently blank.

"Will it really?" She was completely fed up now. "They're not going to win, Nick."

"How do you know? Strange things happen all the time."

"Yeah, like us going somewhere romantic for a change."

"You'll enjoy the second half, I promise," he said calmly, ignoring her jibe.

She wished she could go home, but they'd come in Nick's car and he had the keys.

Kirsty sighed, rubbing her hands together.

"I'm frozen."

He put an arm around her and gave her an encouraging smile.

She felt herself thawing out as she remembered why she loved him. He mightn't be romantic, or Britain's answer to Brad Pitt, but he had a smile that made her heart beat faster, and he was wonderfully warm.

"COME on, come on," Nick muttered, obviously eager for the second half to start.

Kirsty sighed again. If he really loved her, he'd realise how bored she was.

All right, so he got fed up when he went shopping with her, but at least it was warm and dry!

"What's up?" he asked, suddenly noticing all her sighing.

"I'm cold, I'm wet, I'm bored and you —"

"Hold on. Oh, no!" he interrupted. "It can't have broken down now!" He was staring at the scoreboard.

"So what? Won't it show your team making a magnificent comeback in the second half? Don't worry, it won't happen anyway!"

"It might," he said loyally, then shook his head. He looked suddenly awkward and she eyed him suspiciously. Why did he keep glancing at the scoreboard?

"Kirsty . . . I . . ."

"Yes?"

"Nothing. Doesn't matter." He slouched down in his seat, so hunched up that he looked more tortoise than human.

"Go on." Perhaps he'd been going to say something romantic. After all, today was the anniversary of the day they'd met. But, then again, he'd probably forgotten that. Men remembered every score in every match for the last half dozen seasons, but when it came to birthdays and anniversaries, they went blank. Convenient, that.

"Kirsty."

At least her nose wasn't the only red one, she thought unromantically as he turned to face her.

"I didn't mean for it to happen like this."

"It's not your fault it's raining." She felt guilty about being such a grouch when she saw his sorry face. At least he wanted her here with him. It wasn't exactly great entertainment, but better than the ironing, and they were going out this evening, even though he hated fancy restaurants.

"It doesn't matter," she said generously, silently swearing to be glad his only vice was football.

"But it does!" His voice rose and people turned to look at them.

"Kirsty! Listen. No, look!"

"No need to get stroppy."

"I wasn't." He yanked her round till she was looking at the scoreboard. She caught her breath at the message flashing there.

Kirsty, I love you.

And, where it ought to say, *Derby County 1, Nick's team 0,* she saw the most amazing question.

"Will I marry you?" she breathed.

The whole ground seemed to be gazing at them and, to make matters worse, a little row of hearts popped up along the bottom of the board.

Nick was as red as she knew she must be.

"You mean that?"

"Yeah." He squirmed, then took a deep breath. "Football is a game of two halves. So's life. I want you to be my other half."

"Oh." She gulped and hugged him, then kissed him for good measure. He kissed her back, and she was so happy that she didn't even care about all the wolf whistles.

Then the teams came running out again and the rain got worse. Kirsty should have been colder and more miserable than ever but, instead, she snuggled up to her fiancé and began to plan.

He thought life was a game of two halves, did he? And he wanted her to be his other half. Well, tonight, she'd show him how the other half lived. There'd be candles, sweet music, and . . .

And, to make everything perfect, Nick's team made an amazing comeback and scored twice in three minutes. Suddenly, there seemed to be such a lot to cheer about! ❑

Glendalough, Co. Wicklow

GLENDALOUGH means Valley of the Two Lakes and it is these lakes and the surrounding hills which make it such a beautiful spot. St Kevin certainly thought so and settled here in the 6th century to pray and meditate. He was believed to have lived in a cave, since known as St Kevin's Bed, but soon founded a monastic centre. Disciples joined him and Glendalough became famous for Christian scholarship.
Pilgrims still come here and a visitor centre now tells the story of this lovely area.

GLENDALOUGH, CO. WICKLOW: J CAMPBELL KERR

Mother Love

I DIDN'T know I had it. It was a little crumpled after all these years, but the small black and white photograph sent my memory reeling back in time.

"Aunt Phillipa's wedding!" I said aloud to myself, holding it up to the available light in my attic.

The picture was faded and obscure, but the expression on my own twelve-year-old features was crystal clear — acute embarrassment.

There was something pleasing about my discovery — and it was oddly painful, too.

My morose expression, which was more appropriate for a funeral than a wedding, was because of my mother's insistence that I wore my cousin Penny's old party dress with all its elaborate frills and bows.

by Maria Richards

But my torture hadn't ended there.

I'd thought nothing could be worse than that hideous dress until the evening had worn on and Mum had decided to treat everyone with her own rendition of "Hello, Dolly"!

Afterwards, she insisted everyone join in a conga — which, of course, she led.

I complained to my father.

"Nonsense, Jane." He'd smiled at me gently. "Your mother just knows how to enjoy herself — thank goodness. The world would be a glum place without her!"

I hadn't been able to find the old wall lights that I had been searching the attic for, but now, knee deep in memorabilia of every kind, I sat upon a battered old suitcase and let the memories wash over me . . .

I must have spent the whole of my tender years in a

permanent shade of pink, I thought, as I glanced through another batch of dog-eared photos.

My body language betrayed all the frustrations that having had a larger-than-life mother had burdened me with. Mother, I had thought then, was the bane of my life; her only purpose seemed to be to humiliate me.

For instance, she used to pop to the corner shop fully suited, wearing a wide-brimmed, feather-trimmed hat.

"Off to Buckingham Palace, Lilian?" our neighbours used to say, but she had merely smiled in response and graciously waved with her gloved hand.

"Do stand up tall!" Mum had said. "Don't slouch."

At which point I would complain that I'd die if I was made to accompany her to the shops when she was so overdressed.

"Rubbish, Jane," Mum would reply. "There's no such thing as being overdressed. Underdressed, yes, but not over!"

UNFORTUNATELY, I had not been blessed with any brothers or sisters to share my disgrace. Alone at night, I'd lie awake, wondering why I had been cursed with a mother who had acted on stage as a child and who now refused to grow up.

I cringed every time she painted the outside of our home to match the new family car. And when she performed a parachute jump to raise money for the local hospital dressed as Wonder Woman, I couldn't even find it in my heart to congratulate her.

I had been the only teenager at school to grow depressed as the weekends approached. Others looked forward to outings and time with their families. Not me; I'd only felt normal at school.

Saturday mornings had been something of a role-reversal. I was made to watch Mum play in what I had termed as the "old fogies" netball team.

It was then she had labelled me "Complain Jane". She was sure that the reason the team had been forced to play through drizzly rain for near enough a whole season was because my sour expression had induced it!

One morning, having posted the winning goal through the opposition's net three seconds before the final whistle, Mum celebrated in style by jumping about with glee. It was caught on camera by the local newspaper's photographer, and made the front page of the Gazette that evening! My friends had jumped at me the following morning saying how "ace" they thought living with Mum must be.

"You can have her," I remember saying. She was too colourful for me.

Throughout my constant hail of criticism though, Mum had always maintained good humour.

"I am who I am, Jane. I only do what feels right for me. Whatever you do, love, there is always someone there to disapprove. Never be afraid of being different."

She displayed this philosophy in her decision to play an upbeat jazz record at Dad's funeral.

"It was his favourite tune, dear," she had tried to justify when I had been appalled. "He wouldn't have wanted a gathering of glum faces. A celebration, that's what he wanted. A celebration of his life."

At fifteen, the idea of celebrating my father's funeral was alien to me. I had felt more lost than ever.

Turning to pick up an album, I knocked a heavy book which was balancing on a box and it fell to the floor, stirring up a cloud of dust. Coughing, I decided the kitchen was a better place to muse over it, with a nice cup of coffee.

Now I recalled why, almost as soon as I got my first wage packet, I had left a comfortable family home and opted for the refuge of a dark, unfurnished basement flat.

And when David came along and professed undying love for me, I made sure that Cupid's arrow was well and truly implanted before revealing his future mother-in-law.

Then, more than eight years later, Harold had come along for Mum and suddenly we had another wedding to prepare for. Watching them together, I had tried to clear my mind of all pre-conceived notions and prejudice and looked at Mum through Harold's eyes. It had opened up my own.

I had never really thought of missing Mum before, because she had always been mine. Always popping in, bringing home-made food, putting up curtains and unblocking drains.

"I see you drop your sense of independence," Mum had mocked once, "when you drop something down the loo and ask me to fish it out. I hope I'm around to hear you saying the same to your children in twenty years or so."

We had both laughed and it was that day I realised that Mum had shed the ridiculous image that she had worn in my immature mind. Somehow, she had gone from awful to awesome as I had finally reached maturity.

Stirring sugar into my mug of coffee, I sat at the pine kitchen table, and began to flick through the leather-bound wedding album.

The days preceding the wedding were merciless on my nerves. I'd no idea how I was able to stand upright with so little sleep behind me on the big day.

Nevertheless, despite my nerves, everything couldn't have run more smoothly. Oaths were sworn without fluffing, the best man remembered the rings and they were lovingly exchanged.

It was over all too quickly and then the painful goodbyes loomed over me. Mum's hands had reached out for mine, but I had just thrown my arms unashamedly around her.

"I'll miss you." I'd sobbed. "Look after yourself, Mum."

Guardians Of The Glen

WITH shaggy coats and spreading horns,
　　A fearsome breed they seem,
Yet placidly they take their ease
　　By loch and mountain stream.

Unmoved, they stand in wind and rain,
　　Defying stormy weather,
Or wade knee-deep in waters cool
　　When sunset gilds the heather.

They watch intruders in their world,
　　Untroubled by alarm,
Their eyes, beneath a heavy fringe,
　　Inscrutable and calm.

An ancient breed by artists loved,
　　Contented and serene,
They blend with hues of hill and glen
　　In many a Highland scene.

　　　　　　　　　— *Brenda G. Macrow.*

T. Parker.

"Don't be daft." She'd laughed. "You've not lost me. You've gained a new step-father. We'll be round for Sunday lunch when we get back!"

We had held each other for an eternity, tears running down both our cheeks, before she was escorted into the waiting limousine . . .

Just then, the sound of the front door opening and being slammed shut, pulled me from my thoughts.

"Mum, I'm starving!" Jenna, my teenage daughter's voice yelled as she sauntered through the hallway to the kitchen.

"Hi, love." I smiled up at her and, noting the memorabilia on the kitchen table, she glanced over my shoulder.

"Oh, that's Nanna's wedding album," she stated, turning a page or two. Then she laughed.

"Oh, Mum, what do you look like?" Her voice was dripping with disgust and she was twisting her features as though the words she had spoken tasted bitter.

Highland cattle, Torridon.

"What do you mean? That was my favourite outfit! I still have it."

Dropping her sports bag to the floor, Jenna pulled a carton of orange juice from the fridge.

"Mum, it was so over the top! And as for that hat with all those ostrich feathers! I spent the whole day pretending you weren't my mother!"

I turned, mildly amused, and placed my hands mockingly upon my hips.

"It was not over the top, Jen. There is no such thing as being overdressed for a wedding. Underdressed, yes, but not over."

Jenna shook her blonde head in a fashion that could only be described as pitying.

"Sometimes, Mum, you sound just like Nanna."

I glanced down at the photograph of my mother, at her well-preserved beauty, the joy in her smile, and the wisdom in her twinkling blue eyes.

"Do you know something, Jen?" I smiled, suddenly filled with pride. "That's the nicest thing you've ever said to me!" ❑

by Jean Imrie

A Very Special Bear

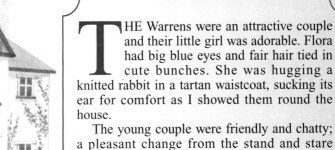

T HE Warrens were an attractive couple and their little girl was adorable. Flora had big blue eyes and fair hair tied in cute bunches. She was hugging a knitted rabbit in a tartan waistcoat, sucking its ear for comfort as I showed them round the house.

The young couple were friendly and chatty; a pleasant change from the stand and stare brigade who wouldn't commit themselves by so much as a sniff.

"And this is the main bedroom." I felt foolish stating the obvious, but none of the viewers so far had given me withering looks.

"What a lovely room!" Mrs Warren exclaimed, going straight to the balconied window, as everyone did. "You can see right across the park.

"Oh, look, Flora!"

Flora followed her mother eagerly.

"Skirrel!" she cried excitedly.

"Oh, we get plenty of squirrels and sometimes a fox."

I glanced at her father, who was looking at the ceiling for cracks that weren't there. Men don't judge houses as homes, it seemed, but as structures that might fall down. He gave me a guilty smile.

"Is the light fitting included?"

I told him it was. With a built-in fan and five bell-shaped shades, it was too big for the seaside flat we were buying.

"And a lot of the furniture's available, if you're interested. We're going from twelve rooms to five, so it won't be possible to take —"

"Teddy!" Flora cried suddenly, homing in on Jimmy Bear, who was sitting on the ottoman.

Putting her knitted rabbit down beside him, she picked the Teddy up, crooning with delight.

Her mother glanced at me anxiously but I smiled back. I didn't mind Flora sharing a cuddle with our old family favourite.

"He's a character," I told Flora, crouching beside her. "He's nearly as old as me. That's why he's a little scruffy."

He was much mended, too. His ears had been sewn back on many times, his feet recovered with red felt and his growl hadn't worked for fifty years, but he had the same bright, friendly eyes and smiling face. He had survived the loving of my children and their children. Now he was honourably retired.

"Boofull. My bubba," Flora enthused, kissing his velvety nose and clasping him tighter.

"Put the Teddy down now, darling," Mrs Warren said gently. "We're going to see the garden. You'll like that."

"Like Teddy! Want Teddy." Flora's lower lip bulged, quivering, and tears shimmered.

"No, darling. It belongs to the lady. Look, here's Scotch Bunny." But, shaking the knitted rabbit at her had no effect.

"Want Teddy!"

"Put it down, Flora," Mr Warren intervened, trying to be firm.

Flora started crying in earnest. It was heart-rending and I felt dreadful. These nice people were probably thinking what a selfish woman I was. What could I want with a Teddy bear?

"You can take him into the garden," I conceded. "Give him a swing."

Both her parents gave me a grateful look. It solved the problem temporarily, at least, as Flora was all smiles again.

As I ushered them out, Mrs Warren picked up Scotch Bunny and shook her head at me, smiling, as if to say, "Kids!"

"I've always wanted a big garden," Mr Warren said, as we stepped outside. There was no mistaking how much he liked ours. His eyes were everywhere, alight with plans.

"That's why we're looking at older properties. Modern houses never have any land."

"It's too much for us now," I admitted. "But here comes my husband. He'll give you the conducted tour."

Eric and Mr Warren were soon deep in conversation, while Mrs Warren lifted Flora on to the swing and rocked it gently. When her mother lifted her off, Flora grabbed hold of Jimmy Bear, kissing the top of his head.

I watched her from the terrace steps, remembering . . .

IT was 1940 and I was six years old.

My mother was holding my hand as we waited for the train to Scotland at Euston Station. The platform was mobbed with people, many of them children like me, with cardboard suitcases and dangling gas marks. Mine had a picture of Felix the cat on the box.

The noise was fearful, as engines clanked and steamed above the clamour of voices and drowned the endless announcements from loud-speakers. Thick, sooty smoke eddied around us, imprisoned by the glass roof.

"Your aunty and uncle will take good care of you," my mother was saying. "They'll be waiting for you at Stirling. You'll love it in the country. There are lots of animals and birds."

So why was she crying?

"Do they have dogs?"

"Three. There'll be puppies to play with."

I was thrilled. We couldn't have pets in the Hendon flat. There wasn't a garden and they'd be terrified of all the bangs and crashes that drove us into the air-raid shelter every night. My mother said they were fireworks, but I knew they were bombs.

A sudden upheaval, like a great wave, rolled along the platform. All the people were craning their necks, looking the same way. Our train was coming!

It was huge and terrifying, a snorting, shrieking monster but I couldn't step back. Too many people were pressing against me.

Porters forced their way through to open the doors.

"Oh, my darling!" my mother cried, picking me up. "Be good. Be happy!"

She kissed me, her face wet against mine. I started to cry, too, as she lifted me through the door and I was nearly bowled over in the rush.

Lugging my suitcase, I dashed into the first compartment and managed to lower the window on its thick leather strap. It crashed all the way down.

My mother seized my hand; I thought she was going to pull me out as people poured in behind me like a burst dam.

"I have something for you!" She thrust a carrier bag through the window.

We hung on to each other until the last possible moment.

"Mind the doors! Mind the doors!" porters shouted, slamming each one.

A whistle blew. The monster train shuddered. The huge wheels started to turn, rumbling in their iron fetters.

"Goodbye! Goodbye! I love you!" my mother called.

I cried as only a child will, in utter abandonment, screaming for my mother as she dwindled to a dot.

A kindly soldier pulled back from the window. He squatted down beside me and tried to mop my face with what looked and smelt like a grubby duster. I squirmed and howled.

"What a bloomin' row!" he said, grinning.

"You sound just like my sergeant with a tank parked on 'is toe. Still got your toes, 'ave yer? Well, you won't 'ave, if you keep that up. They'll all fall off."

He went on talking cheerful nonsense until my sobs turned to hiccups and he caught the glimmer of a smile.

"That's better! Nah then, let's see what yer mum gave yer. Summink nice, I'll bet." He picked up the carrier bag and held it open for me to look inside.

It was full of golden fur, which took shape as I lifted it out. It was the most beautiful Teddy in the world, with pink pads on his paws and a big red bow round his neck! His eyes were friendly and he had a lovely smile.

"Cor!" said the soldier. "It must be Christmas. Ain't 'e a beaut'! Wotcher goin' ter call 'im?"

"Jimmy Bear."

He became my new mummy and I loved him with all my heart.

ERIC and the Warrens were coming towards me now, all smiling.

"Me live here!" Flora shouted. "With Teddy."

So they were going to buy the house. I wasn't surprised.

It was right for them and they'd take good care of it, I was sure. They'd probably have more children to fill the rooms and play in the garden, to climb the trees and perhaps keep a pony in the orchard, as we'd done.

"I'm so pleased," I said, as we all shook hands. "I know you'll be happy here."

"I feel that." Mrs Warren smiled. "We all love it. And when Flora's little brother or sister is born . . ." She gave me a glowing smile.

"I can ring the agents from here," Mr Warren was saying, tapping his mobile phone.

Flora was jumping up and down in front of me, demanding attention.

"Teddy come, too? All mine?"

"She's never done this before," Mrs Warren apologised. "It's very embarrassing. She has lots of toys of her own. I can't think why she's set her heart on yours."

But I could.

"He's absorbed so much love over the years. I think she senses that."

It was time to let go of a sad memory, time to comfort another child.

"Yes," I told Flora, happily seeing her face light up. "Teddy's all yours." ❑

Illustration by Peter Gibson.

Golden Showers

by Emily Neal

A N elegant grey-haired woman pushed the wheelchair into the garden and settled its frail occupant under the rose-strewn pergola. The beautiful blooms hung low as if they were too heavy for their stems. On this hot June day, the cool leafy shade they cast was very welcome.

"Comfortable, Dad?" asked the woman.

"Fine, fine, don't fuss, Elizabeth," said ninety-three-year-old Harold Manston.

Elizabeth got up to leave him in peace, but he put out a hand to detain her.

"Don't go. Sit with me for a bit and enjoy the roses. Have a bit of a rest. There's nothing to rush indoors for, is there?"

Elizabeth eased herself on to the garden seat beside the wheelchair, and held her father's hand. They sat in companionable silence for a while, lost in the study of the rose, a variety named "Golden Showers".

Elizabeth remembered the day they had planted it. They had spent long hours planning the garden and a professional landscape gardener had done the work. Both being so busy in the bakery, they had little time for gardening. Elizabeth, though, enjoyed tasks like dead-heading and pruning, weeding among the shrubs and in the flower borders.

They had chosen Golden Showers to replace another, much older, rose that had grown on the walls of the little yard at the back of the bakehouse where they had lived all through her childhood. That had been yellow, too, with large, single petalled blooms on branching stems. She had loved that rose dearly.

When they moved to a rather fine detached house away from the smell of constant baking, delivery vans and the demanding customers, a yellow rose was almost her first priority. She insisted on planting it herself, watched by the gardener.

Suddenly her father's grip tightened on her hand.

"Would you have married him, Elizabeth?"

Her dad's mind wandered a bit these days but there was no need to wonder who was meant by "him". Elizabeth knew exactly, and why the question came at this moment, on a sunny day in June.

"Yes," she said simply, following his train of thought, humouring him gently.

"Eh, girl, your life could have been so different . . . so very different." Her father sighed deeply.

"I don't regret a minute of it," Elizabeth said crisply. "I've been happy, and busy, and successful. You can't spend your life worrying over whats and ifs."

"All the same . . ." continued Harold. "All the same . . ." His eyes closed as his voice drifted into silence.

He often did this — started a conversation and then wasn't able to continue it but, today, with the dappled sunlight constantly shifting as a gentle breeze played with the rose, Elizabeth was glad to be left with her own thoughts and memories.

IT was in June, long ago, that she had first seen Allen. He stood on the doorstep of the house across the yard from the old bakery, a gangling, red-faced lad in a grey suit that was about four sizes too small. A severe looking man had him by one arm and under the other he held a brown paper parcel.

Elizabeth stared at the visitors and called to her mother who bustled to greet the newcomer.

"Elizabeth, this is Allen. He's coming to work with your father, and learn the baking trade. Allen, this is Elizabeth, my little girl."

The two stared at each other. Elizabeth inwardly squirmed. Little girl, indeed!

The man let go of Allen's arm and left after a word or two with her mother.

Allen continued to stare around him. He seemed bewildered by the girl with dark pigtails, her smiling mother, the sunshine on gleaming windows and the smell from the bakehouse mingling with the smell of a dinner cooking in the welcoming kitchen.

He'd never been in such a place in his life. He felt that at any moment it would all be snatched away and he would find himself back in St Paul's Children's Home, with its smell of sour milk and carbolic soap.

Elizabeth, urged by her mother, took him up to the little room that was to be his very own.

The family home was joined to the bakehouse and shop by a narrow entry over which was a sort of bridge that consisted of a single room with a sloping ceiling. It had two doors, one to the bakehouse loft where huge bags of flour were stored, and another that led on to a landing and the main house.

Elizabeth's mother had distempered the walls of the room in a lemon yellow, and hung yellow-checked curtains at the window. Elizabeth had chosen the two pictures that hung on the walls — both of horses, because she was going through her horse-mad phase at the time.

She said to Allen that he didn't have to keep them; he could put up his own pictures, if he'd rather. He told her he didn't have any pictures, just a Bible, a change of clothing and a ten-shilling note — all gifts from the Master at St Paul's.

Elizabeth felt very sad at the thought of those few belongings. Her own room, with its rose-sprigged wallpaper, was full of things. There were dolls in a cot of their very own and a special Teddy bear on her bed, as well as other soft toys, books, crayons, hair brushes, ribbons and all kinds of treasures collected on her many seaside holidays.

She rushed from the room and, grabbing some books, a soft Panda, and some games, returned to Allen's room and put them on his bed.

"What's all this stuff?"

"For you. You can read in bed, while you cuddle Panda."

"Can't read," Allen muttered. "Not very well, anyway."

Elizabeth was aghast. She didn't know anyone who couldn't read.

"Then I'll just have to teach you," she announced. She was nothing if not practical — something she had inherited from her father.

The weeks and months flew by. Allen blossomed in the caring affection he enjoyed in the Manstons' home.

True to her word, Elizabeth spent some time every day helping him to improve his reading. And Elizabeth's mother helped him to understand the bookkeeping necessary for the running of a small business.

The raw, red-faced orphan grew into a tall, quite handsome and very hard-working apprentice baker. His skin was very fair, and his hair had an attractive reddish tinge to it which often made Elizabeth wonder how his mother could have left him at the Home.

The summer of 1940 arrived and, with it, Allen's eighteenth birthday.

They always celebrated his birthday in June, the month he first arrived, for no-one knew his real date of birth. As a present, Harold had decided to offer his now grown-up apprentice a partnership.

He and his wife couldn't imagine life without him. Allen had become the son they had always wanted. As Harold said, he was well trained, a good bread baker and, for all they knew, someone might offer him a job elsewhere. It would break their hearts if he left them now.

Nor could Elizabeth, now aged fifteen, imagine life without Allen. She loved him dearly.

The cosy reading lessons were long over, but they worked together in the shop during the Saturday rush. They spent time scrubbing down the bakehouse, cleaning tins and organising the equipment, and talked endlessly about the business.

One day they'd expand it, put in a café, perhaps, for the Saturday shoppers. They'd build up the confectionery side and increase deliveries. They never spoke of love, but both knew that their plans were only ever to be carried out together.

Allen felt that Elizabeth was too young to feel as he did. His heart lurched every time her hair brushed his face as she reached for cakes from a high shelf; it thumped at her brilliant smile as she greeted him at the start of the day. How he loved her gentle hand on his shoulder as she wished him goodnight.

He wished such times would never end, and when Harold offered him a partnership, he accepted readily. There was nowhere else in the world he wanted to be.

But there was somewhere else he had to be. Just after his birthday, his call-up papers arrived. We were all taken aback but knew there was nothing we could do to keep Allen at the bakery now. He would have to go . . .

Butterfly Summer

HERE, in the lazy hours of leisure,
　Under the azure summer skies,
Sun-coloured flowers flaunt their treasure,
　Tempting the passing butterflies.

Bright-painted wings on blooms of yellow —
　Beauty so brief too soon departs!
Yet, while it lingers, let the mellow
　Joys of the summer warm our hearts.

Then, in our dreams, when summer's ended,
　Memories sweet will still arise;
Blossoms will bloom, their colours blended
　With the bright wings of butterflies.
　　　　　　　　— *Brenda G. Macrow.*

T. Parker.

ALLEN stood beside the wonderful rambling rose with its yellow blooms, Elizabeth by his side. She was too young; it wasn't the time — but he had to speak. Who knew what the future might hold for either of them?

"Elizabeth, wait for me," he said.

He didn't speak of love, but Elizabeth knew herself to be loved. There was no need for the words he failed to find. She took his hand and held it up to her face.

"Of course I'll wait," she said. "The war will end soon enough, and you'll be back. We'll do all those things we planned." She smiled shyly. "Let's include at least three children, shall we?"

Allen blushed to the roots of his sandy hair.

"I love you, Allen," Elizabeth whispered.

"I love you, too." And he kissed her, very gently, on the lips.

Harold and his wife watched from the kitchen window, fearing that Elizabeth was too young to commit herself. She still had a lot of growing up to do . . .

Allen went off to serve in a field kitchen, where he fed the fighting troops. Elizabeth and her parents waited anxiously for his letters.

Allen described Army life, the difficulties of turning out a decent loaf when they were being strafed by enemy fighters.

They hoped that the tales were exaggerated as they struggled with shortages at home.

They tried to keep up their standards using National flour, no butter or lard, very little dried fruit and even less sugar. Elizabeth shuddered to think what they were forced to put into some of the cakes.

Then her mother fell ill, and the burden of keeping the books and running the shop fell on Elizabeth's shoulders. Her mother slipped away without ever knowing how well her daughter was doing. They mourned her deeply, but carried on working.

Harold's was the only bakery in the town and customers had to have their bread. With the rationing of almost everything, bread was increasingly important. Elizabeth worked, never grumbling, fed her father as well as she could and dreamed of the day when Allen would return home and make everything better.

But he didn't come home.

Harold and Elizabeth had just finished for the day and were sipping a well-earned cup of tea when the letter arrived. She began to read it aloud.

"Dear Harold and Elizabeth,

My mother has got in touch with me through the War Office. She has been bombed out, is ill and homeless. I hope you will see that I have to take care of her, and will forgive me for letting you both down . . ."

She couldn't see the rest of the words as the letter fluttered to the floor. Her father picked up the piece of flimsy paper and continued reading.

"When the war ends, as it will soon, I shall get a job in London and find a house for us. She is glad I have a trade . . ."

Harold snorted angrily.

"I bet she's glad he has a trade to follow. All she wants is his money. What a fool the boy is!"

The rest of the letter was about Allen's joy in discovering his real family, and his roots in London's East End. He hoped they would think well of him . . . but Harold's voice choked on the words.

Elizabeth's eyes clouded over and she stared out of the window to where the rambling rose was just coming into bloom. First her mother, now Allen. She was only eighteen and she felt that she couldn't go on. Life was too cruel.

Harold went out into the bakehouse and banged and crashed among his loaf tins, scrubbing and scouring quite unnecessarily. Without his wife, he had only lived for the day when he could give the business — and possibly his daughter — to Allen to care for.

For many weeks the house became silent with despair. They continued to serve the public but the sparkle had gone out of their lives.

The war came to an end and, although food was still rationed and shortages blighted their lives, Harold's bakery wore a more cheerful face.

Elizabeth decorated the window with a fake iced cake, ribbons and lace, and a notice that she was taking orders for celebration cakes. She acquired the little sweet shop next door and opened the café that she and Allen had spoken of.

They were not far from the public library. Regular readers made a habit of choosing their books and then retiring to Elizabeth's for coffee and a scone, toasted tea cakes or a slice of gateau.

Her enthusiasm began to rub off on Harold. As regulations eased, he became well known for his continental-style breads and rolls. Eventually he took on a confectioner who could turn out gateaux and pastries to supply the shop as well as the café.

They fought off a takeover bid by one of the huge factory bakeries and continued to make good, old-fashioned wholesome bread. They even offered a slicing and wrapping service in order to compete with the cheap white ready-sliced supermarket bread.

They moved to a detached house, putting in a manager at the old house in the yard, and enjoyed their newly landscaped garden. For a while, they scarcely noticed the years fly by.

The fashion for "white sliced" faded. Harold, now suffering from arthritis, was amused by Elizabeth's account of queues on Saturdays for the granary and stoneground breads on sale in his shop. The good bread had always been there, but suddenly it had become fashionable to seek it out.

"Manston's: Traditional Bakers and Confectioners" even made the trendy magazines as being well worth a visit. The business had become a great success and Harold was so very proud of his daughter . . .

HE awoke from his doze with a start.

"It might have all been so different for you, if Allen had come home at the end of the war," he said, taking up where his sentence had faded out.

"But, Dad," she said gently, "he did come home — eventually. Don't you remember? He took good care of his mother until she died, and then he came home, just as he promised." She smiled gently at the memory of that wonderful day.

A drift of petals fluttered down as a gentle breeze stirred the Golden Showers.

"We married, maybe a bit later than we planned, but he was worth the wait. And now we must get back to your only grandson's wedding reception."

"Of course. Young Barry. I'm getting old, Elizabeth. It must have been the roses that brought the war years flooding back. I'm sorry, love. You must think I'm going a bit odd!"

"Look," Elizabeth said, smiling radiantly. "Here's Allen now, come to fetch us in."

A tall white-haired man strode towards them, kissed Elizabeth and wheeled Harold's chair back to their laughter-filled home . . . ❏

IT was now or never, Harry Carpenter thought to himself, watching Jean threading her way up the bus towards him. He could procrastinate no longer. He'd been on his own too long. People were very kind, of course — especially his daughter, Sally; popping over regularly to see if he needed any shopping. Yet, now he'd been a widower for several years, he suddenly realised he should make more of an effort to look after himself. And perhaps it was time he made new friends, got out a bit more.

Jean Browne was just lovely, he thought, as she joined him with a cheery smile. Always so well turned out.

Jean was someone Harry felt he could really talk to and, since her fool of a husband had left her, Harry knew she would understand about feeling lonely, too.

Illustration by Gerard Fay.

They often had a chat when he called into her shop to buy groceries, but he never seemed to be able to pluck up the courage to ask her out. Well, it *was* thirty years since he'd been on a date!

Jean was on her way to work and chatted happily to him as the bus approached the village. You could really feel the warmth of that smile and the kindness behind those clear blue eyes.

There was a pause in the conversation and their eyes met. Here goes, thought Harry.

"Jean, I was wondering if you would . . .?" he paused, nervously.

"Yes, Harry?" Her tone was encouraging.

"It would be very nice if we —"

"Jean! Cooee! Jean, dear!" A loud, shrill voice interrupted from behind. A large, flowery dress sailed into view and Harry's heart sank. It

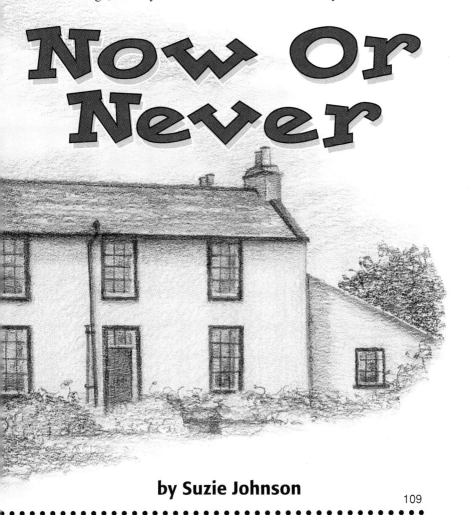

Now Or Never

by Suzie Johnson

was one of Jean's neighbours.

The shrill tones continued in a garrulous monologue and the moment was lost.

Harry sank down in his seat as Jean was regaled with the exploits and adventures of her neighbour's son and daughter and her grandchildren.

Both the son and daughter appeared to have successful, glittering careers and the grandchildren were so advanced in their classes at school that they must surely be geniuses.

In the village centre, Harry escaped into the chemist's to collect his prescription. He glanced down at the shopping list his daughter had written for him. How marvellous she was; she knew exactly when he was running out of some essential item and also seemed to know what little treats he liked. His wife had always done the shopping and he still forgot essentials without a list.

He smiled to himself as he turned the list over and read Sally's note on the back, inviting him for dinner on Sunday. She was so thoughtful.

WHEN he looked up, he saw Jean standing outside her grocery shop, talking to a deliveryman. As the man got back into his van, Harry decided to seize the moment.

He strode purposefully across the road but, as he approached the shop, he heard someone call to Jean, who hurried back inside. She'd obviously not seen him.

Harry carried on walking past when he saw the shop was packed. He couldn't possibly even speak to Jean now, let alone ask her out.

He walked round the shops again, and then a third time, even popping into the newsagent's to pay his paper bill, something he usually did at the end of the month. Anything to stall for time until Jean's shop was empty. He could be in the village all morning at this rate!

As Harry walked past for a third time he saw that, at last, there were no customers in the shop. In he went and there was Jean, a lovely little

---

Cawdor Castle, Inverness-shire

CAWDOR CASTLE boasts an unusual legend. The Thane of Calder, founder of the castle, was told in a dream to load a donkey and build his castle where it led. It stopped beneath a thorn tree, and that is where he began work. Remains of a thorn tree can be found in the vaulted ground floor.

This is an interesting castle to visit and you will have to cross a drawbridge to reach it. Inside, there are impressive fireplaces, tapestries, paintings and family heirlooms. Outside, take time to enjoy the walled gardens, picnic site or nature trails.

CAWDOR CASTLE, INVERNESS-SHIRE: J CAMPBELL KERR

smile twitching her lips and her blue eyes twinkling even more than usual. Surely she hadn't seen him walking up and down? No, she'd been far too busy . . .

Sally's shopping list seemed endless. At last, Jean packed the last item into Harry's bag and handed him his change.

"Is that everything, Harry?" For the second time that day, her voice was warm and encouraging. The shop was still empty, but he faltered.

"No, I . . ." He stopped. He was losing his nerve again. Idiot! He took a deep breath and began again.

"I mean, yes," he corrected himself. "Jean, I'd be very honoured if you —"

CRASH! Apples tumbled from the counter and rolled like marbles across the floor. Plums fell in all directions, like purple billiard balls in slow motion. A large packet of dog biscuits spilled its contents at Harry's feet.

"Benji! Naughty dog! Oh, Jean, I'm ever so sorry — I tied him up outside, but you know how he hates being left, love . . . He slipped his lead . . .Oh, dear, I'm sorry . . . I'll help you, here."

The dog's owner, a plump grey-haired lady in mauve tweed, flapped about apologetically.

Harry fled from the shop, leaving Benji gloriously crunching the dog biscuits. He almost seemed to be smiling.

That was it, Harry decided. Never again. First the garrulous neighbour and now Benji, the crazy dog. He and Jean just weren't meant to be.

He put one hand into his pocket and sighed wearily.

He'd left his shopping list on the counter in Jean's shop. He didn't have a clue what else Sally had put on the list. Suddenly, he felt hopeless.

"Harry! Harry!" It was Jean, self-consciously hurrying towards him. She caught up with him and smiled.

"Harry," she said, rather breathlessly, "thank you so much for your note. I'd love to come out with you. And no, I'm not doing anything on Sunday."

Harry stared, first at Jean and then at the shopping list in her hand. She'd read Sally's message, asking him for dinner — and thought the invitation had been for her!

Harry smiled at Jean in delight and they'd soon made a date.

* * * *

Jean bustled back to her shop. She'd always liked Harry Carpenter. But what a shy man! Walking up and down outside the shop like that. Just as well he'd left behind his shopping list with the note from his daughter on the back!

She smiled to herself. There are times when a shy man needs a little push, aren't there? ❏

by
Jan
Wright

Illustration by Majken Thorsen.

A Curious Christmas

LLIE jumped as she heard her mother call and quickly
closed the old chest lid.
She spun round to give her best ten-year-old smile as
Mum peered into the shed.

"Oh, Ellie, what are you up to now?"

That, of course, was a good question. Ellie hated lying to her
mother, but adults could be very peculiar when it came to
Christmas. So, shrugging her shoulders, she crossed her fingers
as she spoke.

"Just curious, that's all." She knew this would satisfy her
mum, as she was always complaining that Ellie was curious

about everything. She was for ever being told she shouldn't poke around in cupboards — especially other people's. But Ellie could never resist it.

Last week, she'd been allowed into Gran's attic to search through countless old boxes and chests. She'd had a fantastic time going through dusty old books and photos. She'd even seen some of Mum's old school reports — they'd been very funny.

Ellie had asked her gran question after question and she was always given an answer. Her mum said she shouldn't be such a pest, but how was she going to learn otherwise?

"You know this shed isn't a play area, Ellie," her mother said. "Your dad will be very upset if you break anything."

Ellie went back into the garden. Well, she'd seen enough anyway. Her Christmas presents weren't hidden in the shed.

It was only because of her curiosity that she'd seen her mum and dad sneak home yesterday with lots of bags which then mysteriously disappeared. Ellie had decided, as it was only three weeks until Christmas, it had to be her presents.

Now, where would they put them? She just had to know.

Maybe in the garage, she suddenly thought. Slipping in there, she started to rummage around in a box she found at the back.

"Ellie!"

Oh, no, she'd been caught again.

"Sorry," she said. "Just curious." Well, it had worked last time.

"Out of here, young lady. How many times have I told you — curiosity killed the cat?"

Well, thought Ellie resentfully, it was the first time today. Her mum was always saying it. It used to really worry her, so, one day, she'd asked if a cat really did die every time she looked in a cupboard. Everybody had started to laugh at her and her dad had ruffled her hair and told her she could be so sweet. Then he went on to explain it had nothing to do with actual cats, it was just a figure of speech.

She had felt stupid, but how was she supposed to know? Why were adults like that? One minute they treated you like you should know everything, then the next minute it was Christmas and they started to treat you like a baby again.

Take her grandad, for instance. Last week, he'd seemed so desperate to go to see "Daddy Christmas" at the local department store that she'd felt obliged to go with him. Well, he often played Twister with her, and she was sure he didn't really enjoy it, so it seemed only fair.

She'd dutifully put up with Grandad asking her at least a hundred times what she was going to ask Santa for. Though she had felt like telling him she knew Santa wasn't real — it was all pretend for little children.

Two hours they'd queued. Two whole hours! Hadn't adults anything better to do?

Well, she was going to show them how grown up she could be — she was going to search the house until she found her Christmas presents.

Perhaps she could enlist Darren's help. Darren was her young brother but, unfortunately, he still believed in Santa Claus.

She was very tempted to tell him it was all an elaborate lie told by adults to . . . to . . . But that was the trouble, she still hadn't worked out why adults told their children that all the presents came from Santa. Why not just admit they bought them?

It was very puzzling, and Ellie didn't like puzzles she couldn't solve. She had tried to ask her father, but he'd just shaken his head.

"It's just the magic of Christmas," he'd said — whatever that meant.

OF course, Christmas was an exciting time. She loved Christmas, all the presents, the food, no school, but she didn't understand why all the rules changed.

At the Sunday School Christmas party last week she'd asked the vicar why was it, when he always told them it was very wrong to lie, he was now encouraging her to lie to her little brother about Santa. Again, she didn't get a proper answer.

"Ellie, it's Christmas," he'd said. Then, throwing the sack of presents over his shoulder, he'd walked into the hall shouting, "Ho! Ho! Ho!"

"It's Santa! It's Santa!" Darren had cried.

Reluctantly, she'd gone along with the charade, although, to be honest, how anyone failed to recognise the vicar immediately astounded her. But then brothers can be very stupid.

She still wished Mum and Dad had given her a puppy instead of a brother.

No, she would have to find her presents without Darren's help.

Maybe they were in the kitchen, she thought. After all, that was the room with the most cupboards. So, after Sunday lunch, Ellie volunteered to both wash and dry the dishes. That would give her plenty of time to make a thorough search.

"Well, you're always complaining I don't help enough," Ellie told her highly suspicious parents. "So I thought I'd give you both a break today."

She was very put out by their response. Even if her motives weren't entirely honourable, they could at least show some gratitude.

Then, to make matters worse, she put in all that effort just to find there wasn't a single present in any of the cupboards.

Ellie was determined, however, nothing was going to prevent her from finding them.

The understairs cupboard only took a minute to search, and she wouldn't have bothered if she'd known it would only lead to another telling off. It wasn't her fault Darren's box of Lego fell off the shelf — well, not entirely. Darren obviously hadn't put it away properly.

Ellie went upstairs to continue her search. Running up the last three

The Evergreen Garden

Winter Wonders

WHEN winter arrives, we have to depend on evergreens to provide us with welcome greenery in the garden.

Many evergreens bear attractive seasonal flowers and berries, as well as having eye-catching foliage, and have numerous uses in the garden.

You can position them to provide shelter from strong, prevailing winds, giving vital protection to less hardy plants. If you want privacy, they can form effective screening. You can also use them to block out an unsightly view, or disguise less attractive sites in the garden, such as sheds or compost heaps.

The skilful use of evergreens can also create different effects throughout the garden.

If you place darker-leaved shrubs at the back, with lighter colours nearer the centre, this will help to make your garden look more spacious.

Evergreens can also provide a useful background of foliage to highlight colourful displays of flowers throughout the seasons. For this purpose, it's better to avoid shrubs with strongly variegated foliage.

Where space isn't a problem, the choice of evergreens is vast. Where quick screening is the aim, some of the faster-growing conifers are excellent. If the bushes are required to brighten up dark corners of the garden, varieties with golden-coloured foliage are ideal.

For evergreens with striking flowers, *rhododendrons* and *camellias* must be the top choice. They won't thrive in chalky soils, but this problem can be overcome by growing them in tubs with slightly acidic compost.

Many of the hebes, too, have lovely flowers. These shrubs range in size from dwarfs only a few inches high, to bushes which can reach over 10 feet. Some of them are slightly tender, but on the

...en

by Alex Muir

Rhododendron.

Pieris.

with white flowers in June, but the bright red, orange or yellow berries are their most striking feature. These appear in abundance in the autumn and give rise to the pyracantha's common name of the firethorn bush.

Although the pyracantha can grow out in the open garden, where it can form a large bush about 12 feet high, it's more commonly grown against a wall. Take care when handling the branches as they have sharp thorns.

A smaller evergreen with attractive berries is the *pernettya* or prickly heath. There are several varieties, carrying either white, pink or red berries right through the winter.

My own favourite from all the evergreens has to be the *pieris*. This slow-growing shrub produces long sprays of white flowers in spring, but they are not its main attraction. This comes from the young foliage which is bright red in colouring.
It lasts for several weeks, gradually fading to pale yellow then a fresh, bright green.

whole they're very easy to cultivate. Varieties such as *"Autumn Glory"* and *"Midsummer Beauty"* can be in bloom for several months.

For an evergreen with coloured berries, a *pyracantha* is an obvious choice. The bushes are clothed steps, she caught her foot and fell face down on the landing.

"You OK, Ellie?" her mum shouted.

"I'm fine," she replied. Oh, yes, she was absolutely great. She'd completely forgotten about the old wicker chest on the landing, but there it was — straight in front of her nose.

The presents were in there. Ellie just knew it. She lay very quiet for a minute or two, listening. She could hear the telly, so she held her breath and prayed nobody would interrupt her. If she was caught again, she'd be in big trouble.

Carefully removing the baskets of flowers from the top, she gently inched up the lid. She slowly lifted up an old curtain and . . . yes, there they were.

Scattered amongst Darren's presents, which weren't worth looking at, were heaps of goodies for her. She could see the personal CD player she'd just happened to point out to her mum a few weeks ago. There was the latest Disney video and her Man United calendar.

It was so exciting. Moving a few things, she saw the annual she'd given so many hints about and a jewellery kit.

Suddenly, she heard a door open. Heart thumping, she covered up the presents, closed the lid, and was in her bedroom before she dared to breathe again.

Bouncing on her bed in excitement, she grinned. She'd found them. She was so pleased with herself . . . Or was she? Suddenly, she wasn't so sure.

A WEEK before Christmas, Ellie was helping her mother decorate the tree. They draped the tinsel and hung up lots of pretty baubles and some chocolate angels she'd be allowed to eat after Boxing Day. She'd always loved this part of Christmas; it always made her feel all cosy inside.

After they'd switched on the fairy lights, she sat looking up at the tree for a long time. Why, she kept asking herself, didn't it feel quite the same this year?

Darren was constantly saying that "Daddy Christmas" was coming. All her school friends could talk about were the presents they might be getting. She knew she should be as excited as everyone else, but she wasn't.

It was a Christmas tradition that one present for each member of the family was placed under the tree several days ahead of Christmas; that way you had a whole week to look at it. Her mum always made sure it was something you could never guess, no matter how much you rattled it or held it up to the light.

Later that evening, once all the presents were in place, Ellie crept into the sitting-room to take a quick look at her present. Tingling with expectation, she picked it up. It was a square box and it only took her a

T. Parker.

A Cat's Life

THEY laze in sweet contentment
On sunlit summer days,
Their claws, in sheaths of velvet,
Well-hidden from our gaze.

They purr and rub against us
And almost seem to smile —
So lovable, so graceful,
So innocent of guile!

Yet, when the sun is sleeping
And light turns silver-grey,
They prowl among the shadows
To hunt unwary prey;

Or, with their night-eyes shining
Like glow-worms in the gloom,
They gather on the roof-tops
To serenade the moon!

Strange creatures, so appealing,
They live a life apart,
So clever at concealing
The tiger in the heart!
— *Brenda G. Macrow.*

second to recognise it. No, she thought angrily, I want it to be a surprise. But it was no good, she knew it was the jewellery kit.

"Caught you," her mum said, sneaking into the room behind Ellie, as she always did.

Playfully putting her arms around her daughter, she laughed.

"How many times have I told you, curiosity killed the cat?"

Ellie slowly placed her present back under the tree.

"Yes, Mum, I understand that now," she said, trying hard not to show her disappointment. She'd learnt her lesson the hard way. Christmas was supposed to be full of surprises and she'd ruined it. Well, next year, she wouldn't be so childish. Next year, she wouldn't even take a peek in the chest, no matter how tempting it was.

As Ellie started to turn away from the Christmas tree, she caught a glimpse of a present with Gran's name on it. Of course, Gran! How could she have forgotten? She still had all her grandparents' presents to open on Christmas morning, and she didn't have the slightest idea what any of those would be.

With a much happier heart, Ellie skipped out of the room. Her gran and grandad always bought her such lovely things; she couldn't wait to find out what they were.

Now, Ellie thought, they've only got a small bungalow. There can't be many places to hide presents. I wonder where they are . . . ❏

MY sister, Estelle, and I were watching one of those old black and white weepies. Her cheeks glistened with tears as she delved once more into the tissue box conveniently on her lap.

"Oh, how romantic. Wasn't it lovely, Zena?" She sniffed and once again I wondered how she survived in this big bad world.

Estelle was a true romantic — a Victorian heroine trapped in a modern body. As we steered into the twenty-first century, I despaired of her facing cruel reality. The boys she went out with didn't have a clue how to deal with someone who expected a knight in shining armour.

But then along came Tristram Jones!

She met Tristram when he helped her change the wheel of her car after a puncture, so he was already high in the white charger stakes.

"He could have been a homicidal maniac, waiting for some helpless female to break down," I argued as she prepared to go out with him.

But Estelle assured me that he was a perfect gentleman.

I must say he was good looking in a dreamy sort of way. He had soft blond hair that flopped over his forehead like a little boy's and his eyes were a baby blue and crinkled at the edges as he gazed at my sister. They seemed made for each other, but I had an uncomfortable feeling that he was too good to be true.

The next day, instead of the huge bouquet sent by her

Sorts!

by
Christine
Evans

121

last boyfriend, she received a single rose with the message: *To my perfect flower.* How soppy!

The following day she arrived home with a small chocolate heart with, *You have melted my heart* written on the card.

"Couldn't he afford a box?" I said but, bathed in her dream of romance, she wasn't listening.

The following weeks saw the romance blossom. My sister drifted round in a state of smiling euphoria.

Call me sceptical, but I kept wondering just how perfect Mr Tristram Jones was. Although, I'll admit, the more I saw of him, the more genuine he appeared.

"What are his family like?" I asked, curious as to who was responsible for such a wonder.

"I haven't actually met them," my sister said so quietly I detected a hint of unease in her voice.

"But you've been going out for weeks! Has he mentioned them?"

"Not really," she muttered and alarm bells began ringing in my head.

"I hope he's not married," I said and instantly regretted it.

A pale look of dismay crossed my sister's face and I hoped, for her sake, that our hero wasn't tangled up with someone else.

Tristram had gone on a course with his firm for a few days. My sister was nervously quiet until she went to meet him on his return. She arrived home radiant, with a huge, fluffy bunny carrying a heart saying, *Missed you.*

I ask you! He'd only been gone for three days!

"I'm going to tea at his home on Sunday." She laughed. "Isn't that wonderful?"

I must say I was relieved.

"So you'll meet all the family?" I asked.

"Just his parents. His brother is away on holiday."

ESTELLE returned from Sunday lunch at Tristram parents, happy but puzzled.

"His parents are so sweet," she explained, "so like Tristram. They made me feel really welcome. But, every time they mentioned his brother, Lancelot, Tristram suddenly changed the subject."

"Lancelot? Perhaps he's out killing dragons and they don't approve of him slaughtering endangered species?"

Estelle wasn't amused.

In the weeks that followed, I began to worry about the size of our house. Not that it's small — it's just that Tristram had decided to display his affection in a new way — with bunnies.

There were big ones, small ones, china ones, more fluffy ones — I was in danger of becoming allergic to fluffiness. But my sister was living in a miasma of happiness and I was glad for her.

My parents loved Tristram. Mum said it was lovely to meet a young man with manners. Dad was pleased that he had prospects.

Everything flowed smoothly — until the night he was late.

They'd arranged to go out for a meal and Estelle was sitting waiting for him to arrive. As the time ticked on she became nervous.

He still hadn't shown up over an hour later. She waited near the phone, darted to the window whenever we heard a car engine and in between times sat pale on the settee, her hands wrung white on her lap.

"Something's happened," she said, when no-one answered her phone call to his home. "Do you think we should phone the hospital?"

"For goodness sake! It's only been a couple of hours," I tried to reassure her. "He probably had to work late."

"He usually rings," she answered anxiously.

I was well used to my boyfriends watching the end of a football match on television before they bothered to pick me up. But Tristram had always been on time and, as we listened to the clock's uneasy tick, I became anxious for her myself.

We were listening so hard for a car that we both jumped when the phone rang. Estelle grabbed it and began answering breathlessly with a series of yeses.

"He's all right! He's all right!" she shouted joyfully when she'd finished. "His car's broken down.

"His brother's been helping him mend it. He didn't think it would take as long as it did to fix. He'll have to get a spare part tomorrow. His brother's driving him over."

"Yes!" I shouted and jumped up and hugged my sister.

The next moment, despite myself, we were waltzing around the room with relief and happiness. We were still flushed and excited when Tristram arrived with his brother in a sleek silver car. We both stared.

Beside my sister's hero was a loose copy of him. His hair was darker than his brother's and cut in a sharp, modern style. Not that I took much notice, of course, but his eyes were a deeper blue. They were alight with a wry smile.

"Meet my brother, Lance," Tristram said.

"You never told me you had a twin." Estelle was surprised. "You only said you had a brother."

"Oh, we're not twins. We're just cursed with the same good looks," Lance said cheekily. "He never tells anyone about me! He's afraid I'll cramp his style."

"I didn't want Lance to frighten you off." His brother sounded sheepish.

"No, he didn't want you to find out we had a cynic in the family until you were well hooked." Lance laughed.

He had a nice chocolatey, deep voice — not that I was listening closely, you understand. If Tristram had seen his brother as a rival, he needn't have worried — Lance wasn't Estelle's type at all.

"I thought it would be nice if Lance could come for a meal, to thank him for his help with the car," Tristram said. "Perhaps Zena would like to come, too? Then Lance wouldn't have to play gooseberry."

I looked down at my leather trousers and then at my sister's pretty dress. Then I noticed Tristram's shirt and tie and Lance's check shirt and jeans.

"We could go to a pizza place." Estelle had noticed my look and caught Tristram's eyes with a smiling look of conspiracy.

We had a great night. While Estelle and Tristram held hands and gazed at each other, Lance and I argued the failings of the local football team and discussed the merits of rock against pop. He called my car a heap; I called his flash but impractical.

"Oh, don't argue, you two." Estelle sounded anxious.

"We're not arguing, just indulging in constructive discussion," Lance said and we both laughed. We had the same sense of humour — just a bit louder than my sister's.

THE next couple of days my sister didn't see Tristram, who was fixing his car.

Then he and Lance arrived and suggested we all go to see a film. Estelle and Tristram wanted to see a romantic comedy, but Lance and I baulked at that, so we split up and he and I went to watch the latest sci-fi blockbuster.

Tristram bought my sister a heart-shaped box of chocolates. Lance bought toffees with my approval.

After the films we met up again, but on the way back to the car my sister and Tristram dropped behind.

"What do you make of those two — mushy or what?" Lance laughed. "I never thought my brother would meet a girl on the same soppy wavelength as himself."

"They're certainly the last of the romantics," I said. "But it would almost be a pity for them to wise up."

"I'm not much of a romantic myself, I'm afraid," he said.

"Me, neither," I confessed. "You can only have so many fluffy bunnies in a family."

"But I have my moments," he added, smiling and squeezing my hand.

"I'd like to be around when they happen," I answered, returning his smile and the hand squeeze.

Estelle keeps pointing to frothy concoctions of lace in the wedding magazines and looks disappointed when I tell her I'd like a silky sheath dress. She thinks our double wedding will be the "most romantic, sweetest, loveliest ever".

I think a double wedding is a good idea, too . . . but for purely practical reasons, of course. ❏

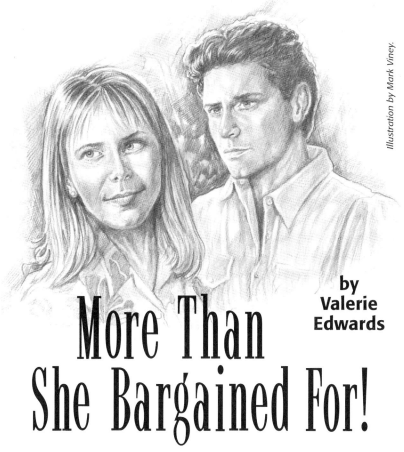

More Than She Bargained For!

by Valerie Edwards

DARN, Penny thought, irritated, when she opened the bread bin, ready for her breakfast toast. How could she have forgotten she'd used the last of the bread yesterday? And that the coffee, milk and biscuits had all been polished off when Mum had call round unexpectedly?

They'd had endless cups of coffee as Agnes had told her daughter it was high time she forgot Dave and found herself a nice young man.

Penny looked in the fridge. It was practically empty, too. And the very last thing she wanted to do on a Saturday was go to the supermarket. It'll be full of families and people queuing to buy a lottery ticket, she thought with a sigh.

She picked up her jacket — she may as well go now, before it got too busy.

She knew the whole trip was doomed when her car refused to start. She had a strong temptation to kick it!

It had been an eighteenth birthday present from her parents and was now well past its sell-by date. So am I, she told herself gloomily. In two years' time I'll be thirty!

The car finally started and she edged out into the traffic.

She got the trolley with the wonky wheel, of course. She'd accidentally steered it into the back of an elderly man's knees and the side of the tobacco kiosk before she got the hang of it.

She apologised to the old man, who promptly smiled and started chatting, until gathered up by his gimlet-eyed wife.

Penny wheeled determinedly past the exotic fruit.

Dave had loved mango and papaya and she had made him innumerable fresh fruit salads when they'd been dating. Maybe his latest love was even now slicing and cubing, she thought wryly. Really, she'd had a lucky escape.

She manoeuvred round a small boy and reached for a carton of semi-skimmed milk. As she put it in her trolley, she saw the kiwi fruit in the corner. She picked it up, puzzled. Perhaps it had been there when she'd collected the trolley. Shrugging, she returned it to the fruit section.

Wheeling past the same small boy again — you didn't see that sort of carroty hair much these days, she thought absently — she added a jar of coffee to the milk. That was when she saw she now also had a box of Aunt Mabel's Frozen Sausage Rolls and a packet of six Snicker bars in her trolley.

Irritated, she glared along the aisle and saw the now familiar carrot-top reaching up for a box of Shreddies.

It must have been him — there was no-one else near. She headed towards him but he saw her coming and vanished. Parents, she fumed. He must have been left to run riot. At this rate, she'd never get the wretched shopping done.

Turning her trolley to return the unwanted items, Penny managed to catch her ankle sharply with a wheel and gasped out in pain.

Now thoroughly cross, she limped to the freezers and wearily found the right place for Aunt Mabel's Sausage Rolls and dropped the box in.

It was at that moment that she saw a man taking the arm of the small boy and marching him down the aisle.

EXCUSE me!" she called out, waving the Snicker bars. She hobbled towards them. It could only be his father, she thought, pain still shooting through her foot and making her even more irritated. Same wretched red hair.

"I think these must be yours," Penny said icily.

The man looked puzzled and shook his head.

"No, you must have the wrong —"

"Well, it was your child who picked them up." She put the chocolate back on to a nearby sweets stand.

"You should keep an eye on him," she couldn't help adding, as she struggled to regain control of her trolley and her balance.

The man looked concerned.

"He hasn't kicked your leg, has he?"

"Oh, no. But he's been putting stuff into my trolley."

"Oh, I'm sorry," the man said contritely.

"Mummy's in hospital," the boy volunteered suddenly. "We're getting the shopping."

Suddenly, Penny felt guilty. She shouldn't have made such a fuss.

"We're not doing very well," the man went on. "Even though we've got a list. I can't find anything!"

Penny could see his trolley was still nearly empty. She knew her way around this store — maybe she should help. She wasn't in a hurry, after all.

"Come on," she said after a moment. "Let me help."

"What a relief." He grinned. "Here. What's this? Do you know?" He handed her the list.

"*A pz ham and pine*," she read aloud. "That's a pizza with ham and pineapple topping."

"Who'd have guessed?" He sighed.

"A woman," she told him. "We all use the same shorthand."

A S they worked their way around the store, Penny began to enjoy herself.

Even when the mischievous little boy put yet another unwanted item in her own trolley, she let it pass. Anyway, she told herself, she'd never tried Aaron's Speciality Pork Pie before.

As they walked towards the check-outs, she paused to look at her own few items. It wasn't much fun shopping for one.

They went to different cashiers but, as usual, she'd chosen the wrong one and he was through and packing his purchases into carrier bags before she'd paid.

He waited for her.

"I hope your wife will soon be OK," she told him as they walked towards the exit.

"Oh, she's not my wife!"

"Partner then," she amended.

"She's my sister," he told her. "I'm just looking after Daniel and trying to keep everything afloat till she comes home tomorrow."

"Oh." She couldn't help feeling pleased.

"I usually just shop for one as well," he went on, giving her a warm smile. "My speciality is scrambled eggs on toast."

"Oh, mine, too," she confessed.

They were in the carpark now, both reluctant to say goodbye.

"I usually do my shopping on Friday evenings," he said tentatively.

"So do I," she admitted. "About seven."

"I'll look out for you," he promised.

She went dreamily on towards her car.

Humming happily to herself, she switched on the ignition. It turned over first time. She breathed a sigh of relief. It was a *very* good omen. ❑

MARSHA WHITHORN peered through the steamed-up window of her cosy flat at the glittering world beyond. "Brrrr!" She turned to shiver at Queenie, her cat, who was curled up on the hearth rug in front of the gas fire. "Been more snow, puss." She found she was smiling, though, for some small part of her still thrilled to the white world outside. She remembered snowball fights and sledge rides down Mulberry hill, icy flakes melting on the tip of one's tongue and snow angels on the lawn.

Her thoughts turned to lunch and the pile of vegetables waiting in the kitchen. A nice pot of soup was just what was needed to stave off the cold, but it seemed such a lot of trouble for one.

"Why look, puss," she said now, "there's young Ben and he's got Private Bob with him."

At the mention of her sworn enemy, the cat stretched and rearranged herself with a disapproving glare at her mistress. Marsha

Getting To Know You

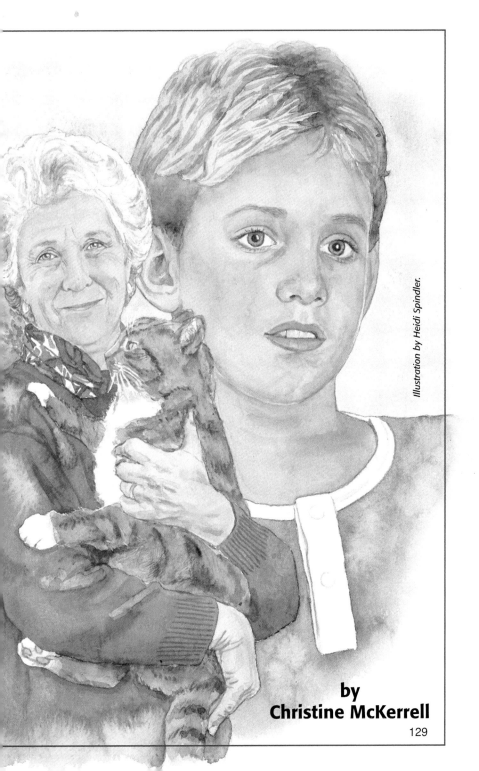

Illustration by Heidi Spindler.

**by
Christine McKerrell**

129

Whithorn chuckled. Really! The animals in Linnet Close were every bit as stand-offish as their owners.

"You'd think we could live together in harmony," she mused, "rather than indifference." She considered the bright new sheltered housing complex and thought of the Major at number two. She doubted if he'd ever made snow angels!

The Major owned Private Bob. He'd taken up residence in the quiet cul-de-sac near the river the day after Marsha herself. There had been the usual polite exchanges, offers of tea on her part, lifts to town on the Major's, but neither had come to anything.

Then there was Miss Shipley in number three, Mrs Cook in four, Albert Dale in five and Miss Horner in six.

THERE'D been no shortage of interest in the new flats. They were completely self contained, if a little on the small side, Marsha allowed, and beautifully warm. Each opened on to a shared hallway and had its own sitting-room, bedroom, bathroom and kitchen. So there was no need at all for the six residents to bother with one another.

Marsha often thought it a pity that the planners' vision hadn't included a communal dining-area. Sitting at table together dispels all sorts of social barriers, she reflected. There was, however, the lounge. That spacious apartment was lodged at the centre of the complex, its one large picture window looking out on to the quiet street.

She'd shaken her head at the pale gold carpet and light beige upholstery on the scatter of easy chairs, thinking that first day that it wouldn't be long before muddy boots and carelessly held coffee cups wreaked havoc. But she'd been wrong. It was still immaculate after several months.

Albert Dale did sometimes drag one of the pale wooden coffee tables up to the window and work away at his complicated jigsaw puzzles. Miss Shipley from time to time entertained one of her old pupils from the school where she'd been headmistress. And Mrs Cook could, on occasion, be spied through the double glass doors, head bent over the intricate needlework with which she seemed to fill her days.

Marsha always meant to wander in for a chat, but somehow never got round to it.

The trouble, she decided now, was that they'd simply allowed the silences to grow until they had assumed almost insurmountable proportions. Where did one start? She glanced beyond the clouded glass to where the boy was carefully feeding Christmas cards into the post box and smiled. Thank goodness for Ben, that's all she could say!

At her window in number four, Mrs Cook also wore a smile on her apple round face. Such a lovely child, Ben Conor! So lucky she'd spied him on his way to fetch the Major's dog for its daily run in the park.

"Ben, dear," she'd called to him as he'd passed by, a bundle of neatly-addressed Christmas cards at the ready. "You couldn't just pop these in the post, could you? It's all that snow." She'd gestured helplessly. "A bit of a thought to go out, you know."

Ben hadn't known, but would never have dreamt of saying so. How could anyone not love snow? He couldn't wait to build a snowman right here on the square of grass in front of Linnet Close. His mum had said she supposed it would be all right.

Mary Conor was resident warden at the close. With the job came a small salary and the tiny warden's cottage at the far end of the complex. The cottage was very important, Ben knew. Since Dad died, they'd had to give up their old house and it wasn't easy, Mum said, finding a decent place where children were welcome.

*   *   *   *

Later that afternoon, Albert Dale lifted his head from a tricky corner of the Sistine chapel and fidgeted in his chair. It wasn't very comfortable.

If it wasn't for the fact the light was better in here . . . Albert's thoughts trailed off. He'd been muttering the same excuses to himself for months now and, even to his own ears, they were beginning to sound a bit lame. The light in the resident's lounge was no better or worse than that in his flat, if truth be told.

With a little whoop of triumph, he fitted another piece of Gabriel's wing into place and thought about tea and the fruit scones Ben's mother had slipped in with the bit of shopping she'd fetched for him. Nice young woman that, he thought, and that lad of hers was friendly, too, come to it. Couldn't build a snowman for toffee, mind!

Albert peered out into the gathering dusk. Now, when he was a lad, by heck, they built snowmen, with a scarf and a pipe and coal for eyes!

In number six, Miss Horner drew a tray out of the oven, greeting the aromatic cloud which wafted upwards with a sigh of sheer pleasure. How she loved the first Christmas pies of the season! The spicy fragrance had her back in the kitchen of her childhood with Mum and Dad and her brother, Miles. Such a fuss over those first mouthfuls, with stray pastry crumbs caught up in the palms of their hands and the fruit inside still piping hot from the oven.

"Make a wish!" their father would roar in his big farmer's voice. "Got to make a wish with the first bite. That's the rule."

Vera Horner smiled at the memory. Such a lot to wish for when you're a child.

She sighed. There was quite a lot to wish for now, too, she thought, as she placed each of the golden pastries on to the cooling tray. It would be nice to share out these mince-pies, for a start.

All the years she'd worked in the accountancy department of the town's large department store, she'd never once thought of herself as lonely. Girls came and went all the time in Halliwell's, but they all thought fondly of Miss Horner and kept in touch, as the row of Christmas cards on the window ledge clearly testified. Two dozen mince-pies hadn't posed a problem then!

She thought of slipping a couple on to a plate for Mr Dale at number five. She'd heard him stomp off down the corridor towards the sitting-room an hour or so since. Off to do one of his puzzles, she supposed. But maybe he wasn't keen on mincemeat. It could be a touch spicy for some. He could always say no, but, then again, perhaps it was better not to intrude . . .

Coming home from the library, her books clutched firmly under one arm, Lilian Shipley sniffed appreciatively as she passed the door of number six. Mince-pies! One never quite forgot the smell. She'd never had much time for baking in all her busy years as headmistress. She could always buy some at the supermarket, she supposed, but somehow they never tasted quite the same.

T HE following morning, at nine o'clock precisely, the Major opened the door of number two and reached down for his newspaper. "Well, I'll be blowed," he muttered, on finding the mat empty. "Paperboy hasn't been." He stooped to fondle the ears of the dog snuffling at his ankles.

"Must be the weather, old chap," he told the spaniel.

Shaking his head, the Major retreated inside, but a cry from the far end of the hall stopped him in his tracks. It was Albert Dale — and he had the morning papers under his arm.

"This 'Telegraph' yours, Major?" he asked. "Found them just inside the front door in a heap. That young rascal of a paperboy's in for an ear-bashing when I get hold of him."

"Thanks, Mr Dale," the Major answered, a puzzled frown clouding his face. "Left in the vestibule, you say? But Mrs Conor always drops them

Snowshill, The Cotswolds

T HIS pretty village is typical of the Cotswolds. Little houses and narrow streets give it an old-fashioned air visitors love.
In the centre of the village, you'll find Snowshill Manor. This National Trust property is well worth a visit to discover the remarkable collection of Charles Paget Wade. Musical instruments, clocks, bicycles and tools are among an amazing assortment of collectables.
There's also a garden — a lovely place to relax on a sunny afternoon.

SNOWSHILL, THE COTSWOLDS: J CAMPBELL KERR

on the mat first thing."

The other man nodded.

"Aye, and the post's still there an' all. She usually pops that through the letterboxes, doesn't she?"

"Just as soon as she gets back from seeing Ben to school," the Major agreed.

While the pair of them were pondering this mystery, the door to number three opened and Miss Shipley appeared, booted and hatted.

"Oh, hello," she cried, spying the two men. "Your heating gone wonky, too, has it?"

"Heating?" they echoed.

"My boiler," Lilian Shipley enlarged. "Tried to get Mrs Conor on the phone, but she's not answering. Something to do with the weather, I expect." She indicated her Wellingtons. "Thought I'd just pop across to the house."

The Major caught Albert Dale's eyes.

"Not answering, eh? Now that is odd. Look here, Mr Dale, why don't we take a turn over to Mrs Conor's?"

Albert nodded.

"Just get my coat," he said, bustling off to number five.

"I'm perfectly capable of going by myself," Lilian protested, while the Major nodded agreement.

"Quite so, Miss Shipley, but it won't harm if Mr Dale and I come, too, now will it?"

The buzz of conversation had reached the ears of the other residents. Soon the ladies from one, four and six joined them.

"Perhaps we should all go?" Miss Horner suggested tentatively.

"No need for that, my dear." The Major shook his head. "No point in six pairs of wet feet!"

"We'll wait in the lounge then, shall we?" Marsha suggested.

As the two men made their way across the courtyard, a flash of colour caught the Major's eye.

"By jove —" he smiled "— that's a splendid snowman young Ben's got there."

Albert Dale grunted.

"Came out first thing after the lad 'ad gone to school. Thought it'd give him a laugh when he gets back."

"Scarf and hat." The Major nodded approvingly. "And a carrot for a nose. Just the job."

"Had to use them little pebbles for eyes, mind. Couldn't get coal. Didn't have a pipe, neither."

"I've an old briar you can use," the other man offered. "Needs a pipe, a snowman does."

They'd arrived at the brightly-painted front door of the warden's cottage but the little house wore the shuttered look that says immediately no-one's home. Albert leaned on the doorbell anyway but no-one came.

"I suppose it's possible Mrs Conor got held up at the school." Albert rapped loudly on the knocker just in case, but the front door remained closed.

"Suppose we'd best get back and tell the others."

IN the lounge, the other four residents of Linnet Close had been speculating on Mrs Conor's non-appearance.

"So unlike her," Miss Horner repeated for the umpteenth time. "She's such a reliable soul."

Mrs Cook nodded.

"And so caring. Goodness knows what I'd do without her to fetch my bits and pieces."

"That goes for all of us," Miss Shipley assured her. "Mind, you," she added thoughtfully, "it wouldn't do any of us harm to get out and about more."

"Not in weather like this, surely," Mrs Cook declared, but Lilian Shipley grimaced.

"Don't tell me you didn't enjoy snow as a child?" she demanded.

Marsha Whithorn nodded agreement.

"Snow angels on the lawn." She smiled. "Pure magic."

Lilian beamed at her neighbour.

"I remember one particular winter, after the college ball, a dozen of us left a fine set in the quadrangle right under the bursar's window. Gave the old chap a bit of a turn in the morning!"

"You might have caught your death!" Mrs Cook protested.

"Could just as likely do that in my flat at the moment," the former headmistress grunted.

"Never mind. Here come the men. Perhaps now we'll find out what's up."

"Bad do," the Major told the assembled company, just as soon as he and Albert had divested themselves of their overcoats. "Met the relief warden on the way in. Seems young Ben's been taken to the local hospital."

"Oh, no!" The distress of everyone present was immediate. They'd all grown very fond of Ben and his mother in the months since Linnet Close had become their home.

"It's not serious, is it?" Alice Cook asked in some trepidation and the Major shook his head.

"'Fraid we don't know as yet. Seems some driver lost control down by the crossing. Caught the lad a glancing blow."

"The poor dear." Vera Horner pressed a hand to her lips. "And his mother, too. She must be frantic."

"Mrs Conor's at the hospital with him. That's why . . ." Miss Shipley waved her hand impatiently.

"Oh, as if a few undelivered newspapers and a dicky boiler matter at a time like this! That poor woman."

"Still took time to contact the office, mind," the Major commented.

"What can we do?" It was Lilian Shipley who voiced the question uppermost in all their minds.

"I've to phone the hospital this afternoon," the Major told them. "We'll know better then."

"And you'll let each of us know?" Vera Horner insisted. But, before the Major could answer, Lilian broke in.

"It seems silly to have you knock on all of our doors when we could meet here."

The others nodded.

"Right-oh. Say four, shall we?"

When he reported back that afternoon and the news wasn't as bad as they'd been dreading, it had only seemed natural for Miss Shipley to bustle back to her kitchen for a pot of tea to help down the mince-pies produced by Miss Horner.

"Just a broken ankle, that's all," the Major assured them. "Be in for a

Faithful Companion

TRUE friend of man throughout his days
  Your every mood he heeds —
To him, the kindly word of praise
Is all he asks, or needs.

He twines his love around your heart,
Unquestioning and true;
Your cat may have a life apart —
Your dog lives just for you.

The world may praise you or condemn,
Exonerate or blame —
It makes no difference to him,
He loves you just the same!

However far afield you roam,
His love will never fail;
What joy, at last, to hurry home
And see him wag his tail.
— *Brenda G. Macrow.*

T. Parker.

few days, poor chap, but home in time for Christmas."

The collective sigh spoke volumes.

"You know," Albert muttered ruefully, "it'll be strange not seeing him about the place."

"Do you think he'll miss the Christmas party at school?" Vera Horner wanted to know. "He was so looking forward to it."

Lilian Shipley clapped a hand to her forehead.

"Never mind the party! What about the carol thingamajig?"

"The singathon," they each echoed amongst themselves, for they'd all signed young Ben's sponsorship form.

"Fifty pence a carol, I promised the lad," Albert said glumly.

"We can let Ben have the money anyway." Mrs Cook shrugged. "It's all in a good cause, after all. New books and equipment for the school library, wasn't it?"

"But there were at least thirty signatures on that form last time Ben showed it to me. He was proud of collecting so many." Miss Shipley sighed. "I suppose," she went on, "we could always go round Ben's sponsors and tell them what's happened. Perhaps they'd still pay up." But she looked doubtful.

"What? You get owt for nowt, my old mum used to say," Albert snorted.

The Major coughed gently.

"I must say I agree with you, Mr Dale. It's too easy to hand money over without thought. No," he mused, "we shall just have to earn it for the boy."

"Earn it?" The other residents of Linnet Court looked bemused and shook their heads in puzzlement.

"And just how do you propose we do that?" Albert Dale demanded and the Major smiled.

"Why, the same way as young Ben," he told them.

Once they'd decided, the whole thing fell into place rather nicely under the Major's command.

"But we can't join in with the school children," Mrs Cook protested.

"No," the Major agreed roundly.

"We could sing in the shopping precinct," Miss Shipley soon suggested. "It's under cover and busy at this time of year."

"I'm sure my old manager at Halliwell's would let us use the front of his store," Vera Horner said enthusiastically.

"Good idea!" Miss Shipley cried. "I'll make a banner, shall I?"

"Can you?" the Major enquired mildly.

"My speciality, you know — art, that is."

"Is it?" Alice Cook gazed at Lilian in admiration. "You know, that's something I've always fancied having a go at. I've always wanted to be able to paint or draw."

"Funny you should say that," Lilian mused with a glance at their surroundings. "This would make rather a splendid venue for a painting class. Good light." She smiled at Mrs Cook. "Would you be interested? I'd say you've a natural talent if what I've seen of those tapestries you sew is anything to go by."

Alice Cook nodded happily, while the Major, sensing control slipping from his grasp, cleared his throat.

"We shall need hymn books," he broke in and little Mrs Cook beamed.

"I'll slip down to St Saviour's this evening and ask Father Graham. I'm sure he'll let us have a few on loan, especially as it's in such a good cause."

"Splendid!" the Major cried. "Pity we can't drum up some music, mind."

"You leave that me." Albert Dale winked. "You wouldn't thank me for my singing, but I'm a dab hand on the old concertina!"

S NOWING again," Marsha Whithorn murmured later that evening as she drew the curtains across the window of number one Linnet Close, smiling as she caught sight of Ben's snowman.

"It's a funny old world, puss," she mused. "This time yesterday, we barely passed the time of day with one another, and now look at us. Carol singing, would you believe! And all because of a bit of snow."

She bustled off to the kitchen, humming "O Come All Ye Faithful" softly under her breath.

"A flask of soup." The Major had nodded at her suggestion. "Splendid idea. Need something to keep the old chill at bay."

Marsha beamed in satisfaction. Was it only yesterday a pot of soup for one had seemed too much effort? Strange that, for six, it was no trouble at all! ❏

With A Little Imagination

by Olwen Richards

I'D never seen Gran's country cottage until now. It was the sort of place you'd expect to be an ancient family home, but in fact she'd only moved in eighteen months ago.

We worried, Mum and I. It might be just a sentimental whim, her moving so soon after losing Grandad. After all, her only link with Little Medford was having spent part of her honeymoon just up the road.

But Gran wasn't the sentimental sort. Living in the country would be cheaper than the city, and healthier, she argued. It would encourage her to get back in the swing of things.

She'd had a routine in the house in Dartford Road for over twenty years. She seemed to understand it would be all too easy to sink inside its comfort and rely on nothing but the TV and her knitting.

Which wasn't Gran at all. She shed her tears over Grandad, then pulled herself together and made up her mind.

"I'm going to start again. Fresh chapter in my life," she said.

And so she did, against Mum's advice. But then she'd never listened to advice, not even Grandad's.

She sent me photographs of Melrose Cottage. I admit it wasn't quite my cup of tea. The place was a bit dilapidated, but there wasn't much an odd-job man could not sort out.

No, it was the scenery I didn't care for. Miles of fen stretching into the horizon at the front. To one side, her solitary neighbour. To the other, a dense and gloomy wood. Here and there along its fringes were a few tall spindly trees, among whose naked tops were clumps of something solid.

"A rookery," Gran told me. "A lovely touch of nature almost on my doorstep."

I was unimpressed. The nearest I usually get to feathers is a pigeon strutting empty-headed across the square outside the office.

However, I was still longing to go down and visit Gran. Not for the rural idyll, but because I was missing her.

The problem was my job. Unless I went all out to make a great impression on the boss, it wasn't going to turn into a career. So holidays were out just now.

"No problem," Gran declared. "I'm not too old to spend a night or two in London!"

"I've no spare bed," I objected.

"And not too old to spend them on a sofa," Gran said feistily.

I couldn't let her. So we waited till my flatmate took a mini break, and used her room.

GRAN positively wore me out. We did galleries, museums and exhibitions at breakneck speed. We moved fast, and we ate fast, too.

"I only wish your mum could see me!" Gran said with a wicked twinkle as she sank her teeth into a burger, dripping cheese.

"She wouldn't be too pleased." I grinned.

"You're leading me astray!" Gran pointed to the chocolate ice-cream gateau on the menu. "Death by cholesterol!

"I think I'll have that and a slice of lemon cheesecake on the side. I mean, I like free range eggs as well as anyone, I'll even have my muesli with skimmed milk, but I do *not* intend to stint on holiday!"

I had a sneaking feeling Gran didn't actually stint at home, unless, of course, Mum was staying. But I didn't say so. Gran was a wiry little bundle of ferocious energy. Who was I to spoil her fun?

I couldn't match her bite for bite, but it was fun to try.

And we shared our gossip, too. My shaky office life, my even wobblier love affairs, her taking to the countryside and village life . . . or not.

"The wildlife round the village is terrific," Gran enthused. "But, well, the people need a bit of getting used to."

I bet they found *she* needed getting used to!

"Mo Morris next door's the worst," Gran went on. "Fanatical about his flowers, and as for veg . . . You'd think he was supplying Nick Nairn, the lengths he goes to for perfection!

"Still —" She shrugged. "He's generous enough. I haven't had to buy so much as a stalk of parsley.

"And his son is handy round the house. Done several bits and bobs for me already. Mind," Gran added briskly, "everything's paid for. No favours. I've made that clear to Mo."

Gran hated favours. Made you obligated, she thought. I felt a fleeting pang of sympathy for Mr Morris and his son.

"The cottage, though," I murmured, channelling the conversation into · safer waters. "It's nice?"

"It will be when I've finished. But you'd not believe the stories . . ."

The headless horseman who was heard to gallop through the garden, the grey-robed monk who knelt beside the wishing well at dusk . . . I smiled. Gran evidently loved the whole shebang, without falling for any of it.

"Mind," she added ruefully, "there is the cherry tree."

I raised an eyebrow.

"A real pain! Comes bursting into flower last spring and wham! Within two days, there's not a blossom left. The wind's had the lot.

"What's more, it's planted far too close. The roots are going to have my wall.

"But nobody will chop it down for me. It was planted fifty years or more ago, when some sweet young girl sought refuge there when her engagement failed, and faded clean away."

"Died of a broken heart?" I put in wistfully.

"Rubbish! The human heart's a lot stronger than we give it credit for, and so is the human imagination!

"The locals think that it'll bring bad luck if I so much as touch that tree, so the wretched thing stands there, sighing and tapping its branches on my parlour window. And legend has it it's the *girl* who comes knocking!"

Personally, I quite liked that idea. Life in London was so horribly prosaic . . .

"You must come down," Gran said.

"I will, I promise. Just as soon as I can," I cried, waving at the disappearing train.

That happened sooner than I thought. Mum rang, in tears. Gran was in Greater Medford Cottage Hospital with a suspected heart attack.

"I can't get down before tomorrow, Jilly."

"I'll go tonight," I said. "Straight after work."

It was already getting dark when I arrived at the cottage. I phoned the hospital. She was doing OK, but it was too late for visiting, so there was nothing for it but to spend the night.

I could see the outline of the cherry tree against the evening sky. Gran was right, it did make sighing noises. I could believe a superstition would grow up . . .

It was the same with that peculiar fog. I told myself it was the way the garden sloped that caused a pocket. Still, if you were in that frame of mind, I guess it could have looked a little like a figure.

And there were thumps and thuds that night, which could have been almost anything including, I suppose, a headless horseman riding by.

I didn't bother getting up to look. Strange houses have strange noises, so I simply pulled the duvet tighter round my ears and tried to sleep.

It was the rapping on the window at dawn that woke me. Not the tree this time — sharper, more insistent.

I got up, pulled the curtain back and then recoiled. A solitary magpie stood on the window-sill! OK, I know it's nonsense, but "one for sorrow . . ."

I scanned the lawn for his mate, in vain.

Gran?

I let the curtain fall and started to get dressed. Ridiculously early, but then . . .

The rapping came again, louder and more urgent. This time it was a giant crow, its plumage glossy black, its eyes glinting evilly.

I shuddered as I fled downstairs to phone the hospital.

"If you could come . . ." the sister said. "She's rambling."

✳   ✳   ✳   ✳

"Delirious, my foot!" Gran muttered, propped against a stack of pillows. "All I did was ask if somebody would see to George and Henry at first light."

"Who?"

"My birds, dear. They come at dawn for breakfast, then I shoo them off before Mo Morris even knows they've been.

"He reckons they're a pest, eating his precious seedlings or whatever. He's just a mean old devil. Can't see beauty when it flies right past him."

"You feed them! So they're not harbingers of death?" I murmured, and Gran gazed at me in exasperation.

"What drivel are you talking now?"

I blushed and glanced at all the high-tech gear surrounding Gran. Suddenly, she laughed.

"It was nothing. Just a scare." She grinned, and reached to pat my hand. "I've always said the human heart is stronger than you give it credit for, remember?"

"And so is my imagination, Gran!" I said happily. And we smiled. ❏

STAR STRUCK

by Jon Harle

B ETH didn't so much come into the house that afternoon as explode into it. Even the dog, who can hear visitors while they're still on the pavement outside, leapt up in alarm. I grimaced as I heard the door vibrating on its rapidly weakening hinges, and tensed myself as Beth hurled her school bag half way upstairs with more vigour than usual.

She appeared in the doorway to the lounge, pink and breathless with excitement.

"Guess what?" she demanded.

"Tell me." I shook my head.

"Well, you know Mr King, our drama teacher? Well, he knows someone who works for the television and they're doing a historical drama and he wants me to go for an audition and he thinks I might get the part if I'm good enough." She paused to draw breath. "And Roberto Verte's going to be in it and I'd be his daughter!"

I stood up and hugged her, amazed.

"Beth, that's brilliant! When are the auditions?"

"Dunno." She shrugged. "Next week, I think. But it's cool, isn't it?"

"You're a star. Can I have your autograph?" I smiled at her.

She tossed her hair dramatically and glided out of the room.

"Ask my agent," she said over her shoulder and I grinned.

I was pleased for her. She was still only a teenager, but had been going to drama classes for a couple of years now. She'd already had a couple of quite important roles in school plays.

I'd always wanted to be an actress myself but had never had the chance. My parents had thought I ought to have a proper job, so I became a physiotherapist. They were probably right, but I still sometimes ached to get up on stage and show off.

"What are you going to wear?" I called through to the kitchen, where I could hear the sound of drawers banging.

She reappeared in the doorway with a bag of crisps and a yoghurt.

"Dunno really. I was thinking about the blue top that Gran gave me and my new black skirt."

"Do you want me to make you an appointment with Stacey on Saturday to get your hair trimmed?"

"OK," she said brightly before disappearing upstairs. I heard her bedroom door shut and then, a few seconds later, the sound of the Backstreet Boys coming through the floorboards.

I sat on the settee and tried to concentrate on my sewing, but all I could think about was Beth's audition. I was so proud of her, but I didn't want to be pushy.

My husband, Paul, gave me the same advice that evening.

"Just let her get on with it herself," he cautioned. "Do you want *me* to take her in to the audition?"

"No, it's OK," I said quickly. "I'm quite looking forward to seeing the inside of a television studio myself. Anyway, I might get to meet Roberto Verte!"

IT was the following Tuesday evening when I took Beth to the TV studios. There were several kids of varying ages there, and a collection of parents.

Some of the mothers were very dressed up — I obviously wasn't the only one secretly hoping to meet Roberto Verte!

But there was no sign of him. There were, however, several assistants running backwards and forwards with clipboards, asking questions and arranging screen tests.

A tall man with dramatic white hair was coming round talking to all the kids and the parents. He introduced himself to us as Alan, the producer, and chatted with us for a few minutes before moving on.

"I think he fancies you," Beth whispered to me.

I shot her a withering glance.

"Well, he seemed more interested in you than me," she added, a bit huffily.

Eventually, Beth was called for her screen test.

After she'd done her test, Alan came back over and talked to us both again. I suddenly realised that Beth might be right — he was paying me a lot of attention.

My ever-subtle daughter caught my eye and winked and I felt myself blushing.

"I'll give you a ring in a couple of days," Alan was saying to me.

"I beg your pardon?"

"To let you know if Beth gets the part."

"Oh, yes, of course," I said awkwardly. "Thanks."

Beth teased me mercilessly all the way home. She seemed more delighted that a TV producer had "chatted up" her mother than the fact that she'd just auditioned for a part in a TV drama.

IN fact, we only had to wait 24 hours. The following evening, the phone rang and Beth answered. I watched her pick up the phone in the vague hope that it might be a call for me, but it obviously wasn't.

She was being very polite, which made me suspicious . . . it obviously wasn't one of her friends. Then I saw her eyes open wide with delight and she looked at me and started frantically giving me a thumbs-up sign and dancing a little jig of excitement while she carried on a normal conversation.

It was when she started talking about rehearsals that I realised who it must be.

"You got the part?" I whispered, and she gave me one of her comical withering glances — as if to say, what else could it be?

"Yes, she's here . . . and thanks very much," she said and handed me the phone.

"It's your secret lover," she mouthed, and wiggled her eyebrows.

"Hello?"

"Hello, it's Alan. I was just phoning to congratulate Beth on her audition last night and to tell her she's got the part of the daughter."

"Oh, that's brilliant!" I was delighted. "I'm really thrilled for her."

"But there's one other thing," he said, a bit cagily. "I know this might sound a bit forward . . ."

Oh, my goodness. What was coming?

"You wouldn't fancy playing a very small part yourself, would you?"

For a moment, I didn't know what to say.

"Who? Me?" I said stupidly.

"Yes, you. I'd love you to play your daughter's mother, if you could. It's just for a few seconds, and you'd obviously look the part!"

I breathed a huge sigh of relief. So he hadn't been eyeing me up for any inappropriate reason! I smiled and quietly told myself off for being so silly . . .

"Would I have to learn any lines?" I asked.

"No, nothing like that," he replied. "All you have to do is stand in a doorway and be kissed by Roberto Verte!" ❏

JOHN clutched his mother's coat and hung on tightly.
He was the man of the house now that his father was away at the war, and he had to look after her in London.

They were on their way to Moorfields Eye Hospital; hopefully the doctors there could help him to see a bit better. Otherwise, they would never have left home on December 23, 1942 . . .

The platform at Euston was crowded. There were soldiers, sailors and airmen carrying kitbags, as well as ordinary Christmas shoppers, hoping

When A Child Is Born

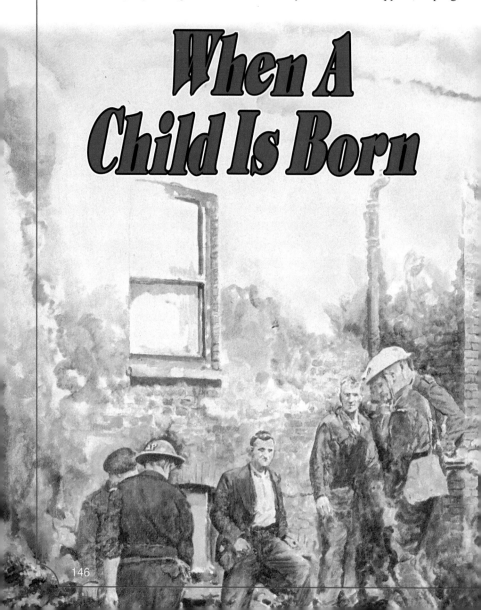

to find a last-minute bargain that wasn't on the rations.

But John only saw a blur of moving shapes and heard the scrunch and thud of heavy Army boots as he tried to steer his mother through the throng.

He didn't want anyone to bang into The Bump, their new baby that was hidden in his mother's tummy until it was ready to be born.

"Shall I give the little boy a hoist up?" a voice shouted over his head. "He looks as if he'll be trodden on any minute."

by Janet Collins

Illustration by Melvyn Warren-Smith.

147

"Oh, I don't know . . ." His mother, Marian, hesitated.

"It's OK, missus. I won't hurt him, and you look as if you need a bit of help."

"Well, thank you, then, if you're sure."

"Sure I'm sure," the airman said as he tossed John up on his shoulder. "How old are you? You're a big bonny lad."

"I'm four," Alan yelled above the noise all round them.

"Four? My word — really grown up." The man grinned. "Where are you off to?"

"He has to have his eyes checked at Moorfields," Marian explained. "I've got the address here. I hope there isn't an air-raid."

"I'll see you safely on your way," the cheerful airman went on. "I'm in no hurry. I'm on leave for a few days."

"Are you sure?" Marian asked. "You must have something better to do with your leave."

"No." The young man's cheerfulness faded briefly as they continued walking. "I got home yesterday and found the house had gone — bombed. Family gone, too — evacuated somewhere."

"I'm so sorry," Marian said. "I wish I could help you."

"I'll find them, don't worry. Bet they're living it up somewhere, safe in the country. Let's get the little boy to his appointment, shall we?"

With the airman's help, they found themselves at Moorfields Hospital in plenty of time for John's eye check, then reluctantly said goodbye to their guide.

The doctor looked at John's eyes and said he'd see clearly after a small operation and with a pair of glasses. They made another appointment to see him in January, then plunged back into the city streets.

There were sandbags everywhere, protecting doorways and bus shelters, and great gaps like stumps of broken teeth where buildings used to be. Firemen and ambulancemen were still searching through the rubble here and there.

Marian hurried John back to the railway station. She found the city depressing and couldn't wait to get back home to her little house at Boxmoor. A warm fire was waiting for them, and a plate of stew with a jacket potato that had cooked slowly in the side oven all day.

Her back was aching, her feet, too, and John seemed exhausted. He said very little about the hospital and his promised operation, but he did ask about the airman.

"Does my daddy look like that man?" he asked. "Does he have the same uniform on?"

"Yes, darling. He looks just like that airman."

"He was kind — just like my daddy — wasn't he?"

"He was very kind," Marian said, wishing he was still there, escorting them through the crowds. It was getting late, and office workers were flocking to the stations to leave London and travel home.

When they reached Euston Station, the wail of the air-raid siren terrified them. Up and down the scale it groaned, as resigned travellers made their way to shelter underground.

Marian, who hadn't been to London since before the war, wasn't sure what to do next. She only wanted to get home.

She made her way to the platform, but nobody seemed to be waiting for the train.

"Better go to the Underground, missus." A porter seemed to appear from nowhere.

"I want the train to Boxmoor," Marian said. "It's supposed to leave at six o'clock."

"No trains till after the raid," the porter explained. "Going to be a big one tonight."

MARIAN made her way to the Underground platform in the wake of hundreds of other shelterers.

It was an astonishing sight. The narrow platform was packed with people lined up like sardines, rolled in blankets, or leaning against every available bit of white tiled wallspace that wasn't hidden by rows of crowded bunk beds. There was hardly room to pick a way to a small space in which to sit.

Everyone seemed to be settling in for a long night. Those who came well-prepared had little Primus stoves and food in baskets, books to read with the aid of torches, or puzzles and games to while away the hours.

Marian swayed on her feet, quite overcome with her own fears, not to mention the pain in her back . . .

"Come and sit here, ducks," a plump Cockney woman called. "Look, I've got a camping chair. Rest your bones. Come on, lovey."

Marian subsided into the camping chair and tried to pull John on to her lap.

"Nah! Put the little chap on the top bunk," the woman said. "He can curl up with my lot."

Up on the top bunk four children of various ages sat eating vinegary chips. John was tossed up to join them and, used to the nightly routine of the shelters, they good-naturedly made room for him without a murmur. They even shared their chips and pulled a frayed, old blanket around his shoulders.

"It's like being in a little boat, Mummy." John grinned at his weary mother.

His companions giggled at his accent, so unlike their cheeky London voices, and they snuggled together to talk about the raids, the bombs, the noise, smoke and fires they had endured in their short little lives. Eventually, they fell asleep, entwined in each other's arms.

Meanwhile, Marian accepted a cup of tea, closed her eyes and surrendered to the pain that now seemed to overwhelm her.

The *Herb* Garden

Fragrant Favourites

NO garden would seem complete without herbs. They bring fragrance, colour and interest to every corner — but can also grow happily in containers, indoors or out.

Annual herbs, such as basil, chervil, dill and parsley, are fairly easy to grow from seed. But many common herbs are perennial and will put on a good show with very little attention.

Why not include thyme, sage, oregano, fennel and chives in your garden? All these herbs can add a unique flavour to many dishes — and give an attractive display in the garden!

Some herbs, though, can be invasive. Mint, for example, is best planted in a container, or could rampage through any garden.

Although you can gather herbs during the summer and dry them off for use over the winter, these dried herbs never have quite the same flavour as those which are freshly picked, do they?

So, every autumn, I plant up two or three containers with a selection of small herbs. Some of them, such as thyme, can be lifted from the garden, but others have to be bought as young pot plants.

Garden shrubs such as rosemary, however, are too large to come indoors!

Once planted, these mixed containers are kept in my porch over the winter.

To ensure they survive indoors, it's essential they have plenty of light and sun. Although they can withstand reasonably cool conditions, they will suffer if the atmosphere is cold and damp.

In fact, indoor herbs should be treated in much the same way as houseplants and should be kept on the dry side over winter. They should only be re-watered when the compost is on the point of drying out.

© *Smith Collection.*

by Alex Muir

the temperature is constant.

If you have a suitable room, with a bright, sunny window-sill, sit them there and try to make them look as attractive as possible. Either plant them in pretty coloured pots, or arrange them in a large trough of mixed plants.

Whichever type of container you select, it's vital that the herbs have plenty of drainage. Place a layer of gravel or broken crockery at the base before you add the compost and choose a soil-based compost for best results.

During the winter, you should be able to enjoy a fresh supply of herbs. There's nothing like picking your own sage and thyme to add to stuffing for the Christmas turkey. And a sprinkling of mint is perfect for the potatoes.

Plan ahead and you'll be able to enjoy fresh, fragrant herbs all year round.

The Perfect Position

THE kitchen is obviously a handy place to keep a supply of herbs, but sometimes conditions there aren't suitable. It can become hot and steamy during the day but, at night, the temperature can fall quite steeply.

Herbs have difficulty coping with such changes. They prefer a position where

But this wasn't an ordinary backache . . . and the baby wasn't due for weeks yet! Marian feared the worst.

She looked frantically at her plump and friendly companion, who understood immediately what was happening. Her hapless husband, Alf, was despatched to find a spare blanket to make a screen, and then to fetch the Salvation Army girl who was patrolling the platform.

Then, while John slept peacefully in his comfortable cocoon with his newfound friends, Marian's little daughter was born, on an Underground platform at Euston Station, in the middle of the blitz.

"It's a little girl," the Salvation Army girl told everyone nearby. "Mother and baby doing well."

A ripple of cheers and soft applause went round and then, somewhere, a mouth-organ softly played a gentle lullaby. Marian smiled gratefully at her very capable midwife.

"What's your name?" she asked.

"I'm Ivy, Ivy Perkins," the Cockney woman said.

"Ivy," Marian murmured. "Ivy . . ."

"I'll call her Holly," she said after a few moments. "And every Christmas, I'll decorate our mantelpiece with ivy, and we'll remember you as we sing that carol — you know the one — 'The Holly and the Ivy'."

"Holly and Ivy." Ivy laughed. "I think that's lovely. I'll put holly on our mantelpiece every year and remember our little Christmas baby. You did know it's Christmas Eve already?"

WHEN John woke up, he was thrilled to see his baby sister. Of course they were moved to hospital as soon as it was considered safe enough, and John was put into a cot beside Marian's bed.

They stayed in hospital for a day or two but, eventually, returned to Boxmoor. There, Holly met all her new relatives and the story of Ivy Perkins and her great kindness was told time and time again . . .

Every year after that, true to her word, Marian decorated her mantelshelf with trailing ivy and, on Christmas Eve, the story of Holly's birthday was retold.

Ivy Perkins became godmother to Holly and kept in touch with the family for the rest of her life. She also kept her promise, always having holly with the finest red berries to decorate her room. Her family were never allowed to forget the night that Holly was born . . .

How do I know? Well, Holly is my grandma (the best there ever was), and Marian, who still lives in the little house at Boxmoor, is my great-grandma. John is my great-uncle — and he has to wear glasses still.

Sadly, Holly never did meet her daddy. He was lost somewhere in World War II. But, Great-uncle John says, of course, he knows all about her, and Ivy. And I'm sure he does, too . . . ❑

MY eyes widened as I listened to my sister, Susie, on the answer-phone. Whatever was she thinking of? Had she gone completely mad? Twelve years younger than me, she'd come up with some hare-brained ideas in her time, but this . . . This one beat them all!

I mean, she knew what my husband was like. At least, she ought to. Clive had been her brother-in-law for more than 25 years. Did she really expect him to agree to her idea?

In a nutshell, Clive is conservative. That's with a small "c". There's nothing unusual in that — but my husband is possibly about as moderate as any man can be.

During the summer, most men are glad to slip into casual shorts and T-shirts — not Clive.

Of course, when not at work, he does dress down, but in his own inimitable style. His tailored shorts sport a knife-edge crease sharp enough to slice an apple and he insists on wearing a white shirt. The topmost button being left undone is his only concession to temperature. To complete the summer outfit, he wears knee-length beige socks and highly-polished brogues.

Most years we holiday in and around Sussex. Although Clive appears oblivious to them, I always notice the occasional strange looks he receives as we browse around the antique fairs we love.

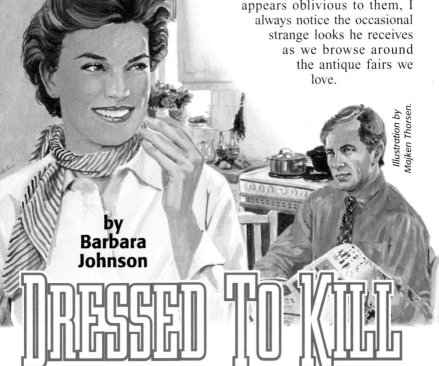

Illustration by Majken Thorsen.

by Barbara Johnson

DRESSED TO KILL

153

I can't help thinking people realise he wears a toupee.

I have suggested — diplomatically, of course — that it resembles a dead ferret, but he says I exaggerate. Although he hadn't said it in so many words, it's my belief that he feels somewhat under-dressed without hair.

CLIVE'S a good, kind man and I love him dearly, despite all his funny little ways. He has always been a good husband and caring father to our two girls, now grown up and married themselves. He works hard, is well-respected at the bank and is unfailingly — as you've probably already guessed — impeccable.

In his spare time, Clive enjoys reading and golf but, as we've grown older, he's begun to share my passion for the garden. Yet, where I'm happy to wear old clothes, up to my elbows in mud, Clive stays perpetually tidy — and is never without gardening gloves and overshoes.

Of course, sometimes his attitude exasperates me. But then I take a deep breath and remind myself of what my mother said to me on the morning of our wedding.

"If there's one piece of advice I'd give you, Martine, it's this. You wed a man for the person he is. Any girl who enters into a relationship with the intention of trying to change her new husband is asking for trouble."

So, instead of criticising, I've tried to understand the reason for Clive's perpetual smartness and have accepted him the way he is.

My husband had the never-a-hair-out-of-place kind of upbringing and — although his parents are no longer here to keep him in line — now he has turned sixty, I doubt if he will ever change.

This was why I was so taken aback by Susie's suggestion. I mean, can you imagine Clive, of all people, agreeing to wear fancy dress?

Susie was organising a party for our parents — to celebrate their wedding anniversary — and thought Mum and Dad would love the idea. They did — but would Clive?

SUSIE rang," I said casually when Clive arrived home from work that night. "She's had a lovely idea for Mum and Dad's anniversary next month." I explained about the party. "And to make it even more fun," I added quickly, "everyone's to go in fancy dress."

Before you could say "Open, sesame!" Clive's face went whiter than our best tablecloth.

"Are you sure that's such a good idea?" he said at last. "I know a party would be nice, but isn't this a little over the top? If my evening suit is cleaned, I think —"

"It still won't be suitable," I finished, attempting a smile. "Even if they are called 'monkey suits'."

"Supposing . . ." He stopped, looking perplexed as he struggled to think up an idea.

Suddenly, the clouded look disappeared.

"I could put a napkin over my arm, briefly, when we first arrive. Long enough to say that I have come as . . . a waiter?"

I shook my head.

"Nice try, but not very original."

Reaching across the table, I put my hand on his.

"Leave it to me, I'll think of something. Promise," I said reassuringly.

I wouldn't let him down. A costume with a little dignity was all that was required.

In the days leading up to the party, no matter how many times Susie probed and pleased, I refused to even hint at what Clive's costume would be. Curiosity was killing her.

When we arrived at the party, my sister's face was a real picture and no mistake. She stared at my slinky, gold lamé evening dress and stiletto heeled sandals.

Then she gazed at Clive, even more impeccable than usual, if it were possible, in his black evening-suit, bow-tie and white silk shirt.

He casually opened his jacket to reveal a holstered toy gun and Susie gasped.

"The name is Bond. James Bond."

And, you know, suddenly, even his toupee looked just fine! ❏

The Show Must Go On!

IF Mum and Dad's dreams had come true, I would have been the next Sarah Bernhardt.

I'd spent most of my childhood wishing my parents had the same hobbies as other people — you know, knitting, do-it-yourself, watching television. But they were both obsessed with amateur dramatics. They were frustrated stars and, having missed the boat themselves, hoped to instil their ambitions in me. But, now I was into my teens, I think they were beginning to realise I wasn't star material after all.

Mum and Dad were stalwarts of SPUDS — St Peter's United Dramatic Society — at the local church.

At various times they produced, wrote, directed, and always acted in, their own productions. The highlight of their year was the annual pantomime and every November they dragged me along to rehearsals. Every year, I managed to avoid a part and ended up selling programmes and raffle tickets.

After various attempts to interest me in acting failed, my parents stopped taking me to the drama club. And I would have been left in peace if it hadn't been for Jody-May Watkins.

Jody-May was the kind of girl who was called to stardom from the cradle. She had fluffy, golden curls and big blue eyes with eyelashes that caused a small whirlwind when they fluttered.

I thought she was a bit over-rated, but those eyelashes started their whirlwind in the heart of my mate, Darren.

"Does she know you, Sandy?" he demanded when she said "Hi" to me one morning at school.

I told him that Jody-May was principal Babe in "Babes in the Wood" which my parents were producing as their next venture into the heady world of drama.

"She's a babe all right!" Darren sighed. It only took him a

by Mary Holloway

Illustration by Pat Gregory.

second to realise that he could be in close proximity to the babe herself if he joined the panto.

He fancied himself as her leading man and was disappointed when I told him that role had gone to Stuart Pool. Stuart was built like a beanpole but, as Dad said, he had a golden voice and, when he crooned to Jody-May at rehearsals, his gangly body was a distant memory.

Still, Darren wanted to chance his luck. Couldn't I take him to rehearsals? He swore he'd do the same for me if I wanted to meet the love of my life.

Darren lived next door. We'd been mates since nursery school and our friendship had sailed along on an even keel until he'd realised I was a girl. Then, suddenly, he wasn't too keen to hang around with me.

It was only the Jody-May factor which had renewed his interest in our friendship — that and the fact that I had a computer.

"Here's your boyfriend, Sandy," Dad said, when he spotted Darren coming up the path that evening.

"He's not my boyfriend, just a mate," I protested. "Anyway, he fancies Jody-May."

But you know how it is when people drop these odd remarks. Suddenly you catch a glimpse of someone from a different angle . . .

I took a good look at Darren as I let him in and realised that he wasn't bad looking. But he was obviously still inflicted with Jody-May fever.

Darren had come round to drop heavy hints to my dad about the panto. Finally, I gave in and took him to rehearsals.

Dad and Mum were playing the woodcutter and his wife, which allowed Dad to direct as well. There was a wicked witch, Red Riding Hood, Robin Hood and his merry men and sundry fairies — plenty of roles to go round. But we soon discovered the show was cast — except for the pantomime wolf! And that needed two "actors".

Like most amateur dramatic groups, SPUDS was always short of cash. This meant that the costumes were either home-made or, only in dire necessity, hired.

In Sadie Bream, Dad reckoned we had a treasure of a wardrobe mistress. She had a limited imagination but was a true genius at saving money and, with a sewing machine and fabric glue, an artiste of rare qualities.

The costume hire shop where she usually went had had a pantomime cow so dilapidated that it was due for the skip. Sadie had begged its carcass and given it a new lease of life, though all those who wore it were asked to tread gingerly in case it disintegrated. Daisy was now a full member of the society.

I'd seen lots of pantomimes as Mum and Dad dragged me along to weigh up the opposition. So I knew the wolf should be a debonair creature, but the creature Sadie had created, from bits and pieces of Daisy, looked more like a demented donkey!

Darren was keen to impress Jody-May and he volunteered his way into the front end of the wolf — I knew I'd be playing the tail end.

Darren tried on the costume. I'd never seen such an exhibition of winking and eye-rolling whenever Jody-May passed by. Next, he had to growl, but his growling was pathetic.

"Louder, louder," Dad said, but the growling was feeble by anybody's standards.

But Darren's downfall was his dancing. Towards the end of the pantomime the wolf had to dance a little jig — impossible for someone with two left feet.

"Do we have to have the dance?" Darren pleaded.

The SPUDS members were horrified. Once the script had been decided by the committee, it was written in stone.

"You give it a try," Dad said, handing me the wolf's head.

Darren looked daggers at me as I put on the heavy, musty wolf/cow's head.

My idea was just to show Darren how it was done but, though I say it myself, I did have a knack with the footwork. My growling was pretty good, too. It was very gratifying to have the cast members praising me, though it was a relief to get back into breathable air.

Darren was livid and would have resigned there and then if Jody-May hadn't coaxed him into being the back end.

ON the night of the first performance, I remembered why I'd backed away from acting. It was one thing to mess about at rehearsals, another to stand in front of an audience. Even though they wouldn't see me behind the wolf's head, my hands were shaking with nerves.

Darren, annoyed at the ignominy of being a wolf's rump, was in no mood to dither.

"Get moving!" he ordered, and pushed me forward.

Then we were on. I staggered through the performance in a grey haze of panic and, miraculously, we hit all our cues. I growled in all the right places and, when the dance, shambled on leaden feet, was finished, we heard a cheer.

Everyone was pleased at how well the panto had been received. Jody-May, whose performance had been exemplary, was euphoric, going round kissing and congratulating all the cast. Darren was purple with pleasure when she came to him.

Stuart Pool got a special round of applause for his singing and I couldn't help thinking he looked good in his costume.

The first performance had gone well, so the next night should have been easier.

It was Saturday and I intended to spend it relaxing. However, Darren phoned to say he was coming round. I spent a few moments in front of the mirror trying to flutter my eyelashes, wondering if I could bowl him over the way I'd seen Jody-May do. But when Mum caught me and asked if I had something in my eye, I knew I didn't have the knack.

Anyway, when Darren did arrive all he wanted to talk about was Jody-May.

I STAYED completely calm until we reached the parish hall that night. But, as soon as we were in the costume and ready to go on stage, panic set in again. I staggered on until the second half, when just as we went on for our dancing scene with the woodcutter, the worst happened. I tripped and Darren tumbled over me.

"There you are, you wicked creature!" Dad shouted, swinging his woodcutter's axe.

Darren pulled himself to his feet too quickly for me and there was a horrendous ripping sound. The audience roared with laughter as Darren grabbed the back of my jeans and dragged me from the stage.

Sadie pulled me into the wings.

"You'll have to go back on your own," she told me. "This lot's past repair." She quickly cut two slits at the front of the suit. "Stick your hands out," she ordered and jammed a pair of fur gloves on them. Then she slapped what I later learnt was parcel tape across my back.

"Don't turn your back to the audience," she said as she pushed me out on stage again.

This was the scene where the wolf promised to behave himself and danced with the woodcutter.

As I stepped out into the spotlight there were several boos from the kids and I felt suddenly relaxed. What more could go wrong now? The worst had happened.

As Dad started his speech, I started sympathetic growls, wild eye-rolling, vigorous nods, subtle whining and an inspired pull on the cow

Kisimul Castle, Barra

THE island of Barra in Scotland's Outer Hebrides boasts a fascinating mediaeval castle. Situated in Castle Bay on a small islet, Kisimul has a long history.

There was a fort here as early as the 11th century but the present building dates from the 15th century. Though it was a stronghold of the Clan MacNeil, they were forced to sell the castle due to debts in 1838. But, in 1937, the 45th Chief of Clan MacNeil, an American, bought back the castle and began to restore it.

Now visitors are welcome and many come, not only to the castle but to enjoy Barra's unrivalled wildlife and peaceful scenery.

KISIMUL CASTLE, BARRA: J CAMPBELL KERR

moo cord. The audience was laughing wildly.

By the time I went into the dance routine, I was Ginger Rogers in a wolf costume.

"You're a star!" Dad said, his eyes misty.

I left the stage in a cloud of euphoria. Unfortunately, there was no-one in the wings to guide me backstage.

I floundered about in the gloom, and suddenly had the vague feeling that I was heading out into the audience. I heard gasps. There were children screaming, chairs crashing, people shouting.

I felt myself falling and there was an almighty crash as I painfully hit the floor.

Everyone began shouting at once and someone pulled the wolf's head from me. I rolled on to my back and saw numerous bewildered faces gazing down at me.

"It's only a girl!" one disappointed youngster said in disgust.

"It's only Sandy," another added.

"Her nose is bleeding," a woman noticed.

Dad leaned over and hauled me to my feet.

"Are you all right, love?" he asked, concerned. "Does anything hurt?"

I shook my head — more dazed than hurt.

"The show goes on," Dad called grandly and everyone cheered.

As everyone assembled for the finale, Darren appeared at my elbow.

"Show off!" he hissed. "Serves you right."

I was shocked — he was supposed to be my friend.

At the end of the finale, I was hauled on stage with Darren. I remember the cheers to this day and it felt wonderful! But I never went on stage again. After my wolf fiasco, even Dad didn't try to persuade me.

But Darren had caught the acting bug and joined the group. Eventually, he ended up with Red Riding Hood.

Jody-May went on to drama school. I think I spotted her in the waiting-room in one of the hospital dramas on TV the other night.

THE next few years were a blur of exams and Saturday jobs for me. I still sold programmes and raffle tickets at the SPUDS productions and at the weekends I worked at the local estate agent's. I obviously impressed the estate agent with the skills of persuasion I'd honed selling those programmes because he offered me a job as a trainee estate agent when I'd finished my exams.

I was in the office one morning when a man came in and hovered by my desk. I smiled vaguely at him and invited him to take a seat.

It was only when I gave him my full attention that I realised he looked familiar. He was very tall, tanned and, if it hadn't been for his mellow voice, I would hardly have recognised Stuart Pool. His once gangly figure now filled out his sharply tailored suit beautifully. He'd obviously had trouble recognising me, too.

"It's Sandy, isn't it?" he said, smiling. "When I saw Alexandra on your name plate I was a bit flummoxed. You look so different nowadays! You always dressed like a boy. I hardly recognised you with long hair and a skirt!"

I must say I had arranged my legs to their best advantage, though I'd never quite mastered the art of fluttering my eyelashes.

"That's my Sunday best name," I said. "But you look so different, too. What have you been doing with yourself?"

He told me he'd been singing on cruise liners, hence the tan, and was looking for a house near his parents. He asked how my parents were and praised Dad for all his encouragement when he was a teenager. We were trying to catch up on old times but the telephone kept interrupting.

"I tell you what, I'll take one of these," he said, picking up our latest house list, "and perhaps we can discuss it over a meal? Then we won't have so many distractions. I know you wouldn't recommend anything unsuitable. You were always such a straightforward girl."

I vaguely remembered him gazing into Jody-May's eyes at the panto. I thought he'd been acting but maybe he'd been victim of the eyelash whirlwind, too.

There was one pearl of a house on the books that I really loved. It was spacious and gracious then and, though we've changed the decor a bit since, it's still a lovely house to live in. Also, it's not too far away from our parents for when Stuart's away at sea.

I changed from selling programmes to houses and now I'm selling my husband's talents as his agent. There's even the promise of a starring role in a musical in the offing. So, at last, Dad has a star in the family! ❏

The Vegetable Garden

Year-Round Crops

THERE'S nothing so rewarding as harvesting your own produce and, with careful planning, your vegetable garden can provide for the kitchen nearly all year round.

Spring, summer and autumn is the time we traditionally enjoy a harvest in the vegetable garden, with early potatoes and salad vegetables giving way to carrots, onions, courgettes — even sweetcorn.

But, once you've lifted your potatoes and lettuces, and harvested the peas, you don't have to leave the ground fallow. Now you have space to plant out some hardy greens, such as winter cabbage, broccoli or kale.

If the soil was well prepared before the early crops were planted, there should still be some nourishment left, so all that's needed is some general fertiliser — at the rate of two to three ounces per square yard.

It can also be helpful to add some sulphate of potash. These winter brassicas will have to withstand harsh conditions and potash encourages the plants to make strong, sturdy growth. About one ounce to the square yard should be sufficient.

If you have been raising your own young plants, they should be ready for transplanting when they are about four to five inches high. Once they are larger than this, they tend to suffer a lot of root damage as they are lifted.

Brassicas need to be planted in firm soil. If it seems loose, shuffle over it with your feet a few times before you start planting.

Winter cabbages and savoys should be set in about 18 inches apart. Kale, broccoli and winter cauliflowers need to be spaced out at two feet intervals.

When the plants are in place, they should be positioned so the lower leaves are just above the surface of the soil. They have to be planted firmly, so use your

ple

by Alex Muir

© Smith Collection.

You may find that there is a waiting list, but don't be deterred. There are many advantages in being able to grow your own produce. It saves you money, everything you eat is really fresh and you can grow varieties of vegetables you especially like.

You'll also be able to enjoy regular exercise in the fresh air and make friends with your fellow allotment holders.

The yearly ground rent of an allotment is very reasonable, and the average size of plot is usually reckoned to provide sufficient produce for a family of four.

And, don't worry if you feel you lack experience. Allotment holders are usually only too pleased to give you guidance and pass on useful tips.

knuckles to press the soil down all around each plant. Then give them a generous watering and wait for a good crop!

A Good Life!

IF you live in a flat or your garden is quite small, why don't you consider becoming the holder of an allotment? Usually you have to apply to your local council, but sometimes they are run by an Allotment Association, so you will have to make enquiries.

by
Alexandra
Blue

Illustration by Gerard Fay.

IN WITH THE NEW

"SOMETHING smells good," Angus McDonald said as he strolled into the large farmhouse kitchen. "Ah! Shortbread fresh out of the oven. My favourite."

"Don't you dare," Jenny warned, slapping his hand when he made to steal a piece. "I need it all for the party tonight."

"Maybe nobody will come," Angus teased, laughing at his wife's stern face.

"Oh, they'll be here." Jenny smiled, checking the clootie dumpling which was boiling away in a large pan on the stove.

She and Angus had held a party on Hogmanay for the last twenty-three years, ever since they were first married, and she couldn't see things changing now.

"You're sounding more cheerful." Angus slipped an arm about her and rested his chin on her dark curls. "Feeling better?"

"A bit," Jenny murmured, blinking back the sudden tears at the sympathy in his voice.

If she kept busy and didn't think about Calum spending Christmas and New Year with his girlfriend's family, she was fine. But whenever she remembered her son's telephone call . . .

"I'd better go and prepare my drinks' cabinet and find the Scottish Country Dance tapes for this evening," Angus said, breaking into her thoughts. "Anything else you need me to do?"

It was usually Calum's job to push back the furniture and set up the lounge for the party. But Jenny had done it herself this year.

"I think we're more or less organised."

"That's what I like to hear." Angus grinned, and went off singing "A Guid New Year" at the top of his voice.

Jenny sighed, her thoughts straying once more to their only child.

Calum was in his final year at university. She was used to him living in Aberdeen and only coming home to Caithness for the holidays to help on the farm. But it had come as a major shock when he announced he wouldn't be joining them for Christmas.

"I've been invited down to Edinburgh to meet Natasha's folks," he'd said, phoning from the flat he shared with some other students. "You won't miss me too much, will you, Mum?"

Of course she'd miss him. They hadn't spent a Christmas apart in all the years since he'd been born.

But Jenny had put on a brave face and said that, as long as he was home to bring in the New Year, she'd be perfectly happy.

"I'll be back before then," Calum had assured her. "Natasha's parents are so busy, I'll probably get chucked out on Boxing Day!"

But they hadn't chucked him out. Calum had phoned to say he was having such a great time, he'd decided to stay on.

"Natasha's family are brilliant," Calum had told her. "Her dad owns his own computer company. Her mum is a management consultant. They're real high flyers but they're incredibly down to earth.

"And you should see the house, Mum. It's a Georgian mansion with ivy growing up the walls. All the bedrooms have en-suites with gold taps and there's white leather sofas and natural wood floors. It's like something out of a magazine."

"It sounds — wonderful," Jenny had stammered, her gaze sweeping over the threadbare hall carpet and the old sofa in the kitchen which was covered with dog hair.

It was maybe just as well Calum hadn't asked to bring Natasha home to meet them. If the girl was used to luxury she might be shocked if she saw the shabby old farmhouse.

"Natasha's mum doesn't like cooking, so we've eaten out most nights," he'd breezed on. "And, at Christmas, they held a party for the neighbours and we had champagne and hors d'oeuvres."

Jenny had giggled.

"Maybe we should give our farmer friends caviar and champagne at the Hogmanay party."

"Er — that's what I wanted to tell you, Mum," Calum had said warily. "I won't be home for New Year.

"Edinburgh is the in place at Hogmanay and Natasha's dad has got us tickets for the party in Princes Street. We'll see live bands playing in the Gardens. You might see me on the television!"

Jenny had thought of their own little party with their friends and neighbouring farmers all dancing and singing in the front room of the farmhouse.

They prided themselves on hosting a traditional Hogmanay with the most handsome farmer in the area first-footing them, and everyone eating black bun and shortbread and enjoying a dram of whisky.

But it seemed that her beloved son had outgrown their style of welcoming in the New Year.

W HEN the first of the neighbours arrived, a log fire was burning brightly in the front room grate, the air was rich with the smell of spicy dumpling, and Andy Stewart was singing "Come in, come in, it's nice tae see ye" on an old tape.

"Did you bring your fiddle, Sam?" Angus asked, taking his friend's coat and ushering him closer to the fire for a heat.

"Of course!" Their neighbour grinned. "I've been practising a few reels and jigs."

Sam's wife, Brenda, pulled a face.

"It's true. He's been that excited about this party he's been scraping away on the fiddle for weeks." She frowned suddenly. "Where's Calum?"

"He's staying with his girlfriend's family in Edinburgh this year." Jenny forced a brave smile. "They're going to the celebrations in Princes Street."

"I suppose that's what happens when they grow up." Brenda sighed, watching her ten-year-old twins getting tucked into the crisps and nuts that Jenny had laid out. "They move on, find their own circle of friends . . ."

"I was hoping he'd accompany me on his guitar like last year," Sam put in crossly. "Silly lad. Imagine missing out on a Caithness Hogmanay."

"Our sentiments exactly." Angus laughed, squeezing Jenny's hand.

An hour later, most of the guests had arrived. It had started to snow and a row of wellies stood at the back door, Sam was belting out "The Hens' March" on the fiddle, and the children were playing with Calum's toy racing cars which Angus had unearthed from the attic and laid out for them in the dining-room.

Someone suggested a Gay Gordons so they pushed the coffee table back against the wall and took their partners for the dance, while Jimmy Shand's music filled the house.

"Are you having a good time?" Angus asked, twirling Jenny round the floor.

"It's a great party," she puffed. "But I wish Calum were here."

"We'll switch on the television later and see if we can spot him in the crowds." Angus smiled.

BY the time they'd danced an Eightsome Reel, which took for ever because they kept getting mixed up, then the local gamekeeper had sung "Campbeltown Loch", and Sam had reduced them all to tears with his playing of a slow air, it was fast approaching midnight.

Angus switched on the television so they could hear the bells and Jenny went through to the kitchen to slice the dumpling and arrange black bun, sultana cake and shortbread on plates.

"You've worked so hard for this party," Brenda said, giving the soup a stir and admiring the home baking. "I don't know how you manage."

"I've had years of practice." Jenny laughed. "And I think it's important to keep the Hogmanay traditions going.

"Calum would probably disagree. But when you see all these young people partying in Edinburgh, well, it's not the same as sitting round the fire, having a ceilidh with your friends, family and neighbours."

"You can't beat an old-fashioned Scottish Hogmanay." Brenda smiled. "I still get a thrill of excitement when someone knocks at the door and presents us with a bit of coal and a slab of shortbread." She paused. "Have you met Calum's girlfriend?"

Jenny shook her head and turned away.

"What's wrong, Jenny? Did I say something to upset you?"

"I'm just feeling sorry for myself," she admitted with a wobbly smile. "I know Calum's a grown man and he's entitled to spend the festive period with his friends, but it was such a shock when he said he wouldn't be joining us this year."

"Of course it was," Brenda soothed.

"And when he described Natasha's folks and their beautiful

K. Price.

house, I began to wonder if he was reluctant to bring her home because we're not sophisticated like them."

"Oh, no!" Brenda was shocked. "Calum's not like that. He'll bring her to meet you both when he's good and ready."

"I suppose." Jenny didn't sound convinced.

"It's good that he wants to experience a different type of Christmas and New Year. It might make him

Flocks On The Fells

ON mountain and moorland
They peacefully graze,
Or follow their leader
Down untrodden ways.

The fox and the eagle
They view with alarm,
And trust to the shepherd
To keep them from harm;

To seek them in snowdrifts
And guard, day by day,
The lost sheep, the black sheep
And those gone astray.

Till, on the green hillside,
When melting streams sing,
We see their lambs gambol
And know that it's spring!
— *Brenda G. Macrow.*

appreciate the traditions we have here," Brenda pointed out sensibly.

"You're right," Jenny said, giving her friend a grateful smile.

"Come on, you two." Angus hurried into the kitchen, almost pushing Frank, the tall, dark, handsome farmer, outside into the snow.

"It's almost midnight. Our first foot is now ready and waiting." He laughed, shutting the door on their shivering neighbour. "Sam is making sure everyone has a drink."

"Did you see Calum in the crowds on television?" Jenny asked, carrying through the plates of food.

"You must be joking! There are thousands of people."

THE children pounced on the clootie dumpling the moment she laid the plate on the table. Brenda had rushed off to the bathroom because it was traditional to have a "clean face and hands" to bring in the New Year. Everyone was shouting, "ten, nine, eight, seven," along with the television announcer.

Then the bells rang out and Jenny found herself swept into her husband's arms.

"Happy New Year, darling," he said, kissing her soundly.

"And many o' them," she returned, laughing when he swung her round and round.

They all started to shake hands and kiss each other while Sam played "A Guid New Year" on the fiddle. Brenda was dancing with her boys. The old shepherd was struggling to unscrew his bottle of whisky to give them all a dram.

"There's someone at the door!" the children shouted.

"I wonder who that could be?" Jenny chucked, imagining their poor neighbour standing on the doorstep in the snow. He had probably been turned into a snowman by now.

But, as she opened the kitchen door, she was surprised to find no-one there.

"Hello?" she called out into the darkness. The wind had died, leaving that odd dull silence that usually accompanies a heavy snow fall. She could hear sheep bleating up on the hill, the cattle moving around in the byre.

"Are you lost, Frank?"

"I'm not lost, Jenny!" His laugh came from the direction of the wood shed. "But I'm no' goin' to be your first foot this year."

"Happy New Year, Mum!" a tall figure declared, emerging from the shadows.

Jenny blinked.

"Calum! Son! Oh, Happy New Year! I'm so pleased to see you," she breathed, pulling him into her arms.

"I thought you were in Edinburgh. We were trying to see you in the crowds."

Gleneagles, Perthshire

FAMOUS for its golf courses, Gleneagles enjoys a stunning location nestling in rolling green hills.

The hotel opened here in 1923 and was used during World War II as a hospital and rehabilitation centre. Now, of course, it is one of the world's most luxurious hotels.

Gleneagles plays host to many famous faces and not all come to play 18 holes. The Mark Phillips Equestrian Centre brings keen horsemen and women and there are other activities, too, including shooting, swimming, croquet and shopping! ➡

"I decided it wasn't really my scene." He smiled. "And I've talked about our old-fashioned, traditional New Year so often, Natasha wanted to experience it for herself. So, we hopped in the car and drove up tonight. If it hadn't been for all that snow, we would have been here ages ago. I know I should have phoned, but we wanted to surprise you."

It was only when Frank had ushered them all indoors out of the snow did his words hit home and Jenny realised they had a surprise guest. Calum turned to put his arm around a young woman and bring her forward to meet his parents.

"Natasha?"

She was nothing like the glamorous, sophisticated young lady she had imagined. Natasha was tiny, like a small bird, with shiny dark hair and huge, frightened dark eyes.

"Hello, Mrs McDonald. I hope you don't mind my arriving like this," she said in a rush. "But Calum was missing you and I really wanted to meet you both and your Hogmanay party sounded just brilliant —"

Jenny burst out laughing. What did it matter if the carpet was worn or that the bed in the guest room hadn't been aired, or that Angus's sheepdog was running through the house with a lump of stolen black bun in her mouth? Her son had just travelled over two hundred miles through the snow so that his girlfriend could experience a warm, Caithness welcome to the year 2002.

"I don't mind in the least," she said, stepping forward to embrace the girl. "Now come with me and meet all our friends."

And, as she walked with Natasha into the front room and saw the fire burning brightly, the Christmas tree glowing in the window, and the rosy happy faces of their friends and neighbours, it struck her that this was probably the best Hogmanay party — ever! ❑

Printed and published in Great Britain by D.C Thomson & Co., Ltd., Dundee, Glasgow and London.
© D. C. Thomson & Co., 2001. While every reasonable care will be taken, neither D. C. Thomson & Co., Ltd.,
nor its agents will accept liability for loss or damage to colour transparencies or
any other material submitted to this publication.
ISBN 0-85116-781-0
EAN 9-780851-167817